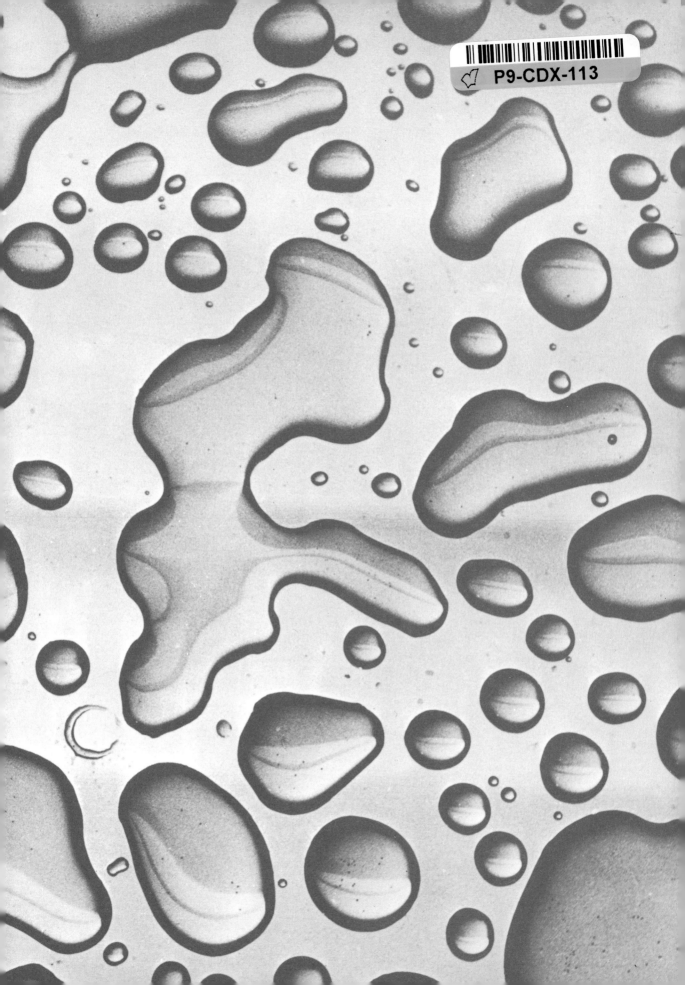

Fresh Water

Delwyn Davies

Fresh Water

The Precious Resource

Nature and Science Library

published for

The American Museum of Natural History

by The Natural History Press/Garden City, New York

The Natural History Press, publishers for The
American Museum of Natural History, is a division
of Doubleday & Company, Inc. The Press is
directed by an editorial board made up of
members of the staff of both the Museum and
Doubleday. The Natural History Press has its
editorial offices at The American Museum of
Natural History, Central Park West at 79th Street,
New York, New York 10024, and its business offices
at 501 Franklin Avenue, Garden City, New York

First published in the United States of America in 1969 by
The Natural History Press, Garden City, New York
in association with Aldus Books Limited

Library of Congress Catalog Card Number 69—17356
© Aldus Books Limited, London, 1967

Printed in Italy by Arnoldo Mondadori, Verona

Contents

Introduction

Fresh water is as essential to life as air, food, and sunlight. Much of the human race is painfully aware of this because it lives in relatively dry countries. In the well-watered parts of Europe and America, however, everyday activity does not center around a struggle for fresh water, and so it is taken very much for granted. We may know from our geography books that little rain falls on much of Asia, Australia, Africa, and many parts of both Americas, yet it is not easy to grasp what this means in human terms. We have water at the turn of a faucet for as little as $48 a year. Thus, it may be hard to believe that in parts of the Near East a housewife may walk over 10 miles each day to fetch a single jar of water for her family. But even in the temperate parts of Europe and America, water supplies are rapidly falling behind the enormous demands of industry, agriculture, and the domestic consumer. Water engineers are now considering how the even greater demands of the future are to be met.

Those who read this book will almost certainly enjoy a piped water supply, and this alone makes it easy to have delusions about the amount of fresh water that is available to sustain life on the world's land masses. The truth is startling: *Very little* of our water is usable at present. About 97.2 per cent exists in the oceans as salt water. The remaining 2.8 per cent is fresh water, but of this, 2.15 is solidified in polar icecaps and glaciers, and cannot be used. Another 0.31 per cent lies so deep in the earth that it is uneconomic to pump it to the surface. We are thus left with a mere 0.34 per cent of the world's total water that can theoretically be used—in rivers, lakes, and in the top half-mile of the earth's crust.

This tiny fraction of the world's total is by no means easy to secure. It represents the amount that would be available if only we could intercept it. Much of it eludes us by draining quickly into the sea by way of rivers and below ground, and still more is wasted because it is too remote from the areas that need it. Almost without exception, there is a wet season with too much water followed by a dry season with too little. There is hardly a single country over which rainfall is evenly distributed. Yet affluent countries use tremendous amounts of water *throughout* the year—in the dry districts as well as in the wet. To overcome these variables we have therefore to store the surplus water of the wet season for use during the dry, and to transport it long distances to where it is needed. Both are very expensive propositions.

In the past, many countries were fatalistic, accepting that the vagaries of climate meant sometimes flood, sometimes drought. However, they are now slowly realizing that drastic steps must be taken if the next generation is not to run seriously short. Gradually, new laws are leading to a more efficient use of water through concentrating on waste prevention and on reuse. Also, new sources are being sought as part of a 10-year survey of water resources, started in 1965, called the International Hydrological Decade. In this book we provide a background to many of the problems that water engineers will encounter. We explain the very unusual properties of this abundant fluid, and trace the history of fresh water from the moment the sun's heat raises it out of the sea to the time when it returns to the sea. We also discuss water supplies, distribution, and purification, as well as the methods by which water can be used several times over before it escapes to the ocean.

94%

95%

96%

Sea water

97.2%

98%

Icecaps and glaciers

99.35%

99.66% Water deep in earth

100% Rivers, lakes, aquifers

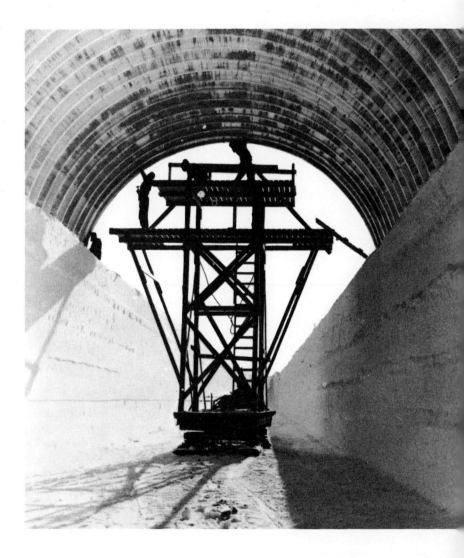

This giant trench cut in ice is part of a village beneath the surface of Greenland. Yet in the midst of millions of tons of ice, a supply of fresh water is an acute problem in polar regions. Because nearby ice becomes polluted, clean ice must be obtained from some distance, and then melted. The fuel cost incurred is so high that the American base at McMurdo Sound in the Antarctic has found it more practical to extract fresh water from the sea by nuclear power. The diagram of the percentage world distribution of water shows that only 0.34 per cent lies in lakes, rivers, and below ground, but even this is not all available at a realistic cost.

1   The Properties of Water

What exactly do we mean when we state that water is a common but unusual substance? Part of the answer was provided by the Greek philosopher Thales as long ago as the sixth century B.C. He stated correctly that, of all substances, water was unusual in existing in all three states of matter while in the natural range of temperature and pressure found on earth. For instance, the upper part of a lake may be *solid* ice, while beneath, it may exist as *liquid*. It also evaporates from the surface of the lake as *gas*, or invisible water vapor.

More than 2000 years later, when scientists began to investigate the physics and chemistry of matter, they examined water in relation to other compounds, and found that it was even more of a puzzle than Thales thought. But they could not account for water's strange behavior until more was known about the atom—the smallest particle possessing the properties of an element—and the nature of the chemical bond.

Any atom consists of a relatively heavy, positively charged *nucleus*, surrounded by one or more light, negatively charged *electrons*. The negative and positive charges balance each other, so that the atom as a whole is electrically neutral. The electrons spin around the nucleus in orbits, but only the electrons in the outer orbit are involved in chemical reactions. The nucleus plays no part at all. We may symbolize the oxygen atom, for instance, like this:

The circles represent the outer orbit of six electrons. (Note, by the way that oxygen has two more electrons on an inner orbit.) Hydrogen, which is the other element in water, has only one electron, and may be indicated:

$$H^{\times}$$

Atoms usually combine with other atoms to form molecules. The atoms may occur in pairs, as in oxygen (O_2) and hydrogen (H_2). Alternatively, the atoms of two or more different elements may join up to form a *compound* with properties unlike those of its constituents. For example, the soft and unstable metal sodium (Na) may combine with the poisonous gas chlorine (Cl) to form a compound—edible table salt (NaCl).

Why is it that atoms combine to form molecules? The answer is that by doing so they become more stable—they form molecules that are less likely to turn into something else. Atoms are most stable when they contain *eight* electrons in their outermost orbit. Hydrogen is exceptional in that it needs only *two* electrons. Let us see how hydrogen attains stability. In the hydrogen molecule, each atom shares its single electron with the other, so that each is surrounded by two electrons, thus:

$$H^{\times}_{\times}H$$

In the case of the water molecule (H_2O), two hydrogen atoms combine with one oxygen atom. Each hydrogen atom thus shares one electron with the oxygen, like this:

$$H^{\times}_{\circ}O^{\circ}_{\circ}{}^{\times}H$$

The combination is stable because two electrons spin around the hydrogen and eight (that is, the six oxygen electrons plus one each of the two hydrogen atoms) around the oxygen. This type of bond, which is called *covalent*, is very strong. It occurs in most organic, and many inorganic, compounds.

Another common type of link between atoms is the *electrovalent bond*, in which atoms lose or gain electrons, instead of sharing them as in the covalent bond. The chlorine atom, for example, has seven outer electrons, while the sodium atom has one outer electron, beneath which lies an orbit of eight electrons. Both chlorine and sodium atoms, remember, are electrically neutral.

Water is unique in that it exists naturally on earth in all three states of matter—solid, liquid, and gas. Solid and liquid states are seen in photograph (right). The clouds are droplets or ice crystals condensed from vapor from the sea.

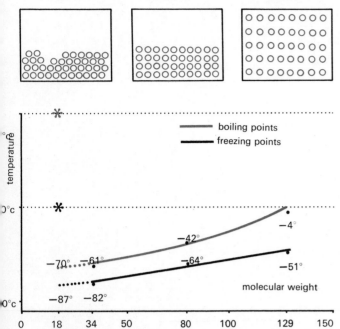

SOLID   LIQUID   GAS

Diagrams show separation of molecules as substance changes from solid to liquid to gas. A solid has its own definite volume, shape, and rigidity. A liquid has a definite volume, but shape is the same as its container. A gas always fills its container. It is not yet certain that water's decrease in density, as temperature rises, is due to the increased separation of its molecules.

boiling points
freezing points

temperature

−42°
−4°
−70° −61°
−64°
−51°

molecular weight

−87° −82°

0   18 34   50   80   100   129   150

H₂O H₂S   H₂Se   H₂Te

The freezing and boiling points (F.P., B.P.) of a compound depend on its structure and molecular weight. Compounds of similar structure and increasing weight show increasing F.P.s and B.P.s—a principle well shown by three hydrogen compounds in graph (left). As we know the molecular weight of water, its F.P. and B.P. should theoretically be found by projecting lines on graph (see dotted lines). But the actual values (asterisks) are very different from what we would expect, suggesting that water has some special property.

But, when sodium and chlorine come together, the surplus sodium electron (which is negative) passes to the chlorine atom. The chlorine atom adds the sodium electron to its seven electrons, now making an orbit of eight electrons. Such atoms, with fewer or more than their natural electrons, are electrically charged. As such, they are called *ions*. The result is a molecule consisting of a positive sodium ion and a negative chlorine ion, which attract each other like the opposite poles of a magnet. The sodium chloride molecule is stable because both ions have eight electrons in their outer orbit.

Now we must look at the forces that hold molecules together. Most molecules exert weak attractive forces on each other, called *van der Waals'* forces. In solids, these hold the atoms together in a very compact pattern. The solid has a definite shape and volume, and also a certain rigidity. The molecules also vibrate slowly. This means that the solid contains heat energy (heat is due to the vibration of molecules), which can be measured as a definite temperature. If a solid is heated above a certain point, the molecules vibrate so fast that they become separated. The molecules thus overcome to a certain extent the weak attractive forces between them. When this happens, the solid

melts to form a liquid. This has definite volume, but almost no rigidity, and the shape of the liquid adjusts to that of the containing vessel. If we heat the liquid sufficiently, the molecules vibrate so quickly that some of them escape from the surface, as a gas—a process called *evaporation*. Finally, the liquid molecules vibrate so fast that the van der Waals' forces are no longer able to keep the molecules together and the whole liquid evaporates, or *vaporizes*, to form a gas.

The temperature at which a solid starts to turn into a liquid—the *melting point*—depends partly on how strong the forces of attraction between the molecules are. This, in turn, depends on the molecular weight, and on how the atoms are arranged within the molecule. The same applies to the *boiling point*, which is the temperature at which the whole liquid turns into a gas. In general, we can say that the higher the molecular weight, the higher the melting and boiling points. It is generally true, too, that different compounds with similar molecular structures behave in much the same way. The melting and boiling points of water should therefore be predictable by comparing the water molecule with molecules that appear to have the same basic structure, like H₂S. But when we do this we find that water

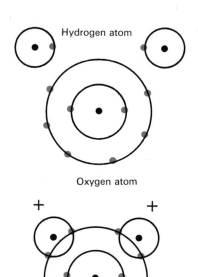

Hydrogen atom

Oxygen atom

+ +

−

WATER MOLECULE

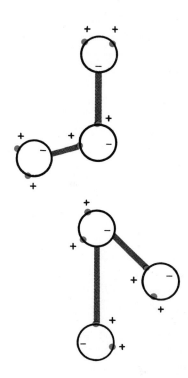

Top left: Diagram of 1 oxygen and 2 hydrogen atoms; nuclei are black dots and electrons blue dots. The oxygen atom needs 8 electrons to be stable but has only 6 in its outer orbit. Hydrogen needs 2 and has only 1. When these atoms combine to form a water molecule (bottom left) they share electrons and become stable. Two positive hydrogen nuclei, however, are then exposed, so that hydrogen ends of molecule are positive and the oxygen end is negative. Adjacent water molecules thus attract each other electrostatically (right) The attractive force is known as the hydrogen bond and results in water molecules linked in groups. Other forces between molecules join these groups into larger ones. It is not known how water molecules are grouped, but the intermolecular forces must be fairly strong because the F.P. and B.P. are very high.

should theoretically freeze at about −100°C. and boil at −80°C. Instead, water freezes at 0°C. and boils at 100°C., as if it were a much heavier molecule with an entirely different structure. There must obviously be something other than van der Waals' forces holding water molecules together and delaying them from parting as the temperature rises.

Let us take another look at the structure of the water molecule:

$$H \overset{\circ\circ}{\underset{\circ\circ}{\overset{\times}{O}\times}} H$$

Although the oxygen and hydrogen atoms share their electrons, oxygen takes an unequal share. That is, the electrons move closer to oxygen than to hydrogen. The oxygen end of the molecule is thus negative and the hydrogen end positive, so that other water molecules join up with the negative oxygen ends attracting the positive hydrogen ends. (See diagram, above.) Water, in fact, exists as *groups* of linked molecules. These groups also form larger groups in a way that we do not yet understand.

These electrostatic forces linking water molecules are called *hydrogen bonds*. They are strong—the heat energy required to overcome the strength of the hydrogen bonds in one liter of

water exceeds 300,000 calories. (A calorie is the amount of heat required at a pressure of one atmosphere to raise the temperature of one gram of water one degree centigrade.) Because the molecules are held together strongly they have to absorb much heat before vibrating into the widely spaced arrangement found in the liquid or gas. The melting and boiling points are thus correspondingly high. However, recent research suggests that the behavior of water molecules may be influenced by other forces as well. There is even some doubt as to the effect of temperature on the separation of water molecules. The exact values of water's melting and boiling points gain significance only when we relate them to the temperatures found on earth. At sea-level, especially in the tropics, the air temperature is relatively not so very far below that of the boiling point of water. This means that considerable quantities of water evaporate from the sea, to be blown by winds across the land. High in the atmosphere, where the temperature is much lower than the freezing point of water, the water vapor turns to ice. Water then falls as snow or hail, which later may turn to rain in the lower regions of the atmosphere.

The fact that hydrogen bonds are fairly strong also partly explains why water absorbs a great quantity of heat to show a small rise in temperature. It takes far more heat to raise the temperature of 10 lb. of water than it would to raise the temperature of 10 lb. of any other commonly occurring substance by the same amount. We say, therefore, that water has a high heat capacity, or *specific heat*. If the specific heat were not so high, the summer temperatures of lakes and oceans would be much higher than they are, and would make them unable to support aquatic life. The high specific heat also has a marked effect in regulating climate by preventing extremes of hot and cold. During the day, some of the heat from the sun is absorbed by water vapor near the ground, thus preventing the air from becoming too hot. During the cooler night, heat is given up by the vapor, which stops the air temperature from falling too much. Another effect of water's high specific heat is that water cools and heats up about five times more slowly than land. That is why coastal areas do not have such an extreme range of temperatures as inland areas in the same latitude. The difference between the specific heats of land and water also accounts for many daily and seasonal wind patterns. Southeast Asia, for instance, is colder than the sea in winter, so that winds blow toward the sea. In summer the pattern is reversed: The land is relatively warmer, and the winds

move onshore, bringing the long-awaited rain.

When ice melts or water boils, they absorb an appreciable amount of heat without showing any rise in temperature. This heat is used solely to change water from one state to another. The amount of heat absorbed on melting amounts to 80 calories per gram, and is called the *latent heat of fusion*. When water turns from liquid to gas, it absorbs 540 calories per gram, this being the *latent heat of vaporization*. Compared with other substances, water's latent heats are extremely high, which is what we should expect after what we know about hydrogen bonds. The change from solid to liquid involves a *partial* separation of the molecules against the attraction of the strong hydrogen bonds. This requires heat energy. The change from liquid to gas, however, involves a *complete* breaking of the hydrogen bonds. Nearly seven times more heat is needed for this change of state. The latent heat absorbed while melting and boiling does not simply disappear. In the reverse process, when water vapor condenses into liquid, every gram gives out the same 540 calories. When water freezes, every gram emits 80 calories.

As water is always changing from one state to another, heat is continuously being produced and absorbed at the earth's surface. This has a great moderating effect on the earth's climate. When

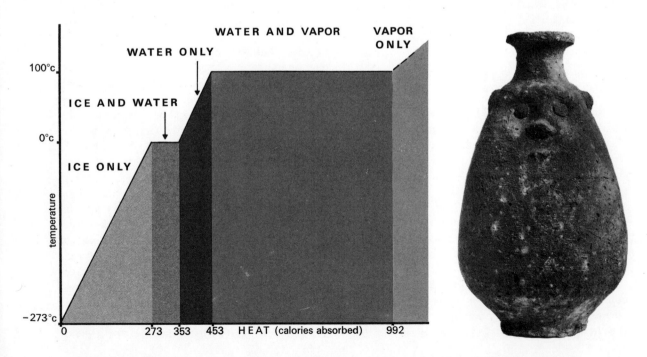

Above: As ice melts it absorbs 80 calories per gram (latent heat of fusion) without showing a rise in temperature. Not until all ice has melted can water's temperature begin to rise. As water turns to steam, it absorbs 540 calories per gram (latent heat of vaporization). Its temperature does not rise above 100°C. until all water has vaporized. The ancient Egyptian wine pot above is sufficiently porous to allow a little wine to seep out and evaporate. This absorbs latent heat from the jar and so cools the wine.

the air temperature falls, water vapor condenses into liquid droplets, heat is given out, and the air temperature rises. When water evaporates on a hot day, it absorbs heat, and the surrounding air is cooled.

Almost all substances become heavier, or more dense, as they approach freezing point. The reason for this is that the molecules come closer together as the temperature falls. But water behaves differently: It is most dense at 4°C., instead of at its freezing point of 0°C. Below 4°C., the density of water decreases because the hydrogen bonds strongly influence the arrangement of the molecules so that they develop large spaces between them. At 0°C., the molecules suddenly arrange themselves into a definite crystalline pattern, in which each oxygen atom is surrounded by four hydrogen atoms. We know this form, of course, as ice.

Water thus *expands* on freezing, and it does so with great force—as some of us know to our cost when we find metal pipes burst by frost. At temperatures far below 0°C., water may freeze in our body's cells and tear them apart. But against these disadvantages we must weigh the advantages. Freezing water splits rock into fragments that fall on to the soil, contributing to its mineral content. In winter, farmers welcome the frost and ice, which break up large clods of earth

into smaller soil crumbs. The fact that water expands on freezing also means that ice is lighter than liquid water, and therefore floats. Imagine what would happen if water were to somehow lose this property. In winter, the Great Lakes of America and Canada, and the upper reaches of the Mississippi and Hudson, for example, would freeze. Ice would sink to the bottom and would not be melted by the sun next summer. Each year, more ice would sink, until finally the amount of liquid water would be appreciably reduced. These waterways would no longer be navigable, and the amount of water available for domestic, agricultural, and industrial use, and for the disposal of sewage, would no longer be sufficient.

The next property of water is its high power of *cohesion*—the power of sticking to itself, also largely due to the strong attractive forces of the hydrogen bonds. It means, for example, that a long column of water does not easily break. A column of fairly pure water needs a force of roughly 2000 pounds per square inch to rupture it. This is very important, because all plants contain columns of rising water in which are dissolved foods for growth. If these columns broke, all plant life would cease, and all animal and human life with it.

Because water has a high cohesive power, it

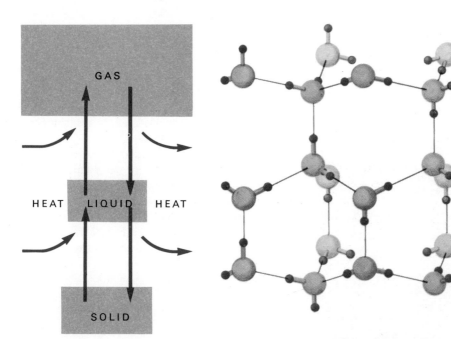

Above: Diagram shows that when water changes from solid to liquid to gas, latent heat is absorbed; and that in the reverse direction, latent heat is emitted.

Water's density increases as temperature falls, reaching a maximum at 4°C. Below 4°C., the influence of intermolecular forces is stronger than the tendency of molecules to compact, and the molecules become widely separated so that the density decreases. At 0°C., water turns to ice with an open crystalline structure (diagram above).

Because water has a high cohesion and surface tension, a falling raindrop (top photograph) is both round and "hard." In fact, such is its bulletlike action that it can gouge a hole in bare soil and throw up particles (photograph above), with several harmful effects. The small soil particles plug the larger soil channels, reducing the infiltration of water and increasing runoff, which washes away the topsoil. Drops sometimes shatter large particles so that they are more easily washed away. Lastly, heavy rain may shift soil toward the bottom of slopes. In many areas, this *splash erosion* (photograph below) is more important than *sheet erosion*, caused by flowing water. The only remedy is to provide plant cover to take the impact of raindrops.

also has (with the exception of mercury) the highest *surface tension* of any common liquid. Surface tension gives water a "skin," as you may have noticed when watching insects walk across the surface of a pond. The reason is that molecules below the surface exert forces of attraction on each other in all directions, and these cancel out. At the surface, however, there is no upward pull to balance the downward pull of the molecules beneath, so the surface is pulled downward.

Let us consider the effect surface tension has on a drop of water. Strong equal forces pull inward all over its surface, and so the drop tends to become a sphere, this being the shape with the smallest surface area. The force of surface tension is so strong that a raindrop resists spreading out at high velocities. One can therefore think of raindrops as being fairly hard. Because of this, rain has a marked effect on many bare soils that lack a shock-absorbing mat of vegetation. A heavy downpour gouges holes in these soils and also closes the tiny openings of the soil channels. The drops then lie on the surface without being absorbed. In time, the holes may merge to form gulleys along which flows water, at the same time carrying away valuable topsoil.

Another special property of water is that it *adheres* to, or wets, many substances. At the side of a glass vessel, for example, water climbs up a short distance because the force of attraction between the water and glass is stronger than the cohesive force below the water surface. In a tube with a very narrow bore, this adhesion makes water rise a considerable distance—a property called *capillarity*. This is very important in nature, for water is thus able to travel through the network of narrow channels in the soil for a short way, to feed plant roots.

One reason why water adheres is that it forms hydrogen bonds with many substances. Glass, for example, consists largely of silica ($SiOs$), whose oxygen atoms join up with the hydrogen ends of the water molecules. In the same way, water strongly wets those soils that have a large component of clay, because clay also contains oxygen atoms combined with silicon.

Finally, we must consider water as a remarkable *solvent*, for it dissolves more substances than any other liquid. To explain what happens when it dissolves electrovalent compounds (p. 12), we can return to the molecule of sodium chloride. In the solid state, salt consists of oppositely charged sodium and chlorine ions held together by electrostatic forces, with small spaces between them. Since water can penetrate between these spaces at the surface of the salt, the water molecules arrange themselves so that their negative ends point toward the positive sodium and their positive ends toward the negative chlorine. This neutralizes the electrostatic forces between the salt ions to a strength of 80 times less than when the salt was solid. There is then little force left to keep the ions together, and they fall apart. In other words, the salt *dissolves*. In the same way, water dissolves over 40 different salts in the sea, and a great many in soil. As a cheap industrial solvent, water is unequaled.

It is no accident that water has these special properties and that the human body is composed of over 60 per cent water. In Chapter 2 we shall examine in more detail the varied roles that water plays in the body. The same principles apply also to plants, on which we all rely directly or indirectly for food.

We are now nearer to understanding why water is basic to life. It is a part of our environment as important as the sun itself and the air we breathe. There is no substitute. No other substance has such unusual properties that make it float when frozen, break up rock and soil, moderate our climate—all properties that make the earth habitable. From the time life began, plants and animals evolved in the presence of water. They are now entirely dependent on it, and man is equally vulnerable. Thales, with whom we began this chapter, certainly had a point when he said, "Water is Best."

Water moving by capillary action in the soil (far left) is important to plants. It moves up toward plant roots in the soil zone and also from the water table. Left: Photograph of a daffodil that was placed in a beaker of black dye and water. Fine black lines appeared on the petals, showing that water automatically rises up the transport tubes in the plant. Continuous columns of water rising up tall trees do not break because of water's high cohesion.

2 The Uses and Distribution of Water

Man has three major thirsts—his own and those of industry and agriculture. We shall give a detailed description of these needs in other chapters, but first we need to appreciate their relative importance. Drinking water is man's most urgent requirement: He may survive several weeks without food, but he would die within a few days if deprived of water. Man is over 60 per cent water by weight, distributed as $26\frac{1}{2}$ liters inside the cells, 12 liters flowing between the cells, and $3\frac{1}{2}$ liters in the blood (1 liter=1000 cc.=about 2.1 pints). We cannot survive long without water because it continuously escapes from the body and therefore needs to be quickly replaced.

The fact that we are over 60 per cent water may seem strange, but not if we recall how versatile a substance it is. It transports to the cells all the necessary nutrients in solution. When these nutrients reach the cells by way of the blood and of the fluid between the cells, they pass into the cells to become part of an active chemical factory in which all reactions occur in water. Here water may play an active role by participating in chemical reactions. It sometimes also acts as a catalyst—that is, a substance that speeds up or otherwise aids chemical reactions without being consumed.

Water also dissolves the oxygen and carbon dioxide that circulate through the body. Cells need oxygen to burn food for energy, and in this process they produce waste carbon dioxide. These gases enter or leave the body through the lungs, but they can do so only if they first dissolve in the moist lining of the lungs. But, as this lining is permanently moist, we lose water vapor every time we breathe out, amounting to about 400 cc. a day.

Another special property of water made use of by the body is its high specific heat. In Chapter 1 we explained how water helped to moderate the climate by absorbing large quantities of heat without showing a large rise in temperature. On a smaller scale, the same applies to the body. Heat produced by cellular activity is absorbed by water without unduly raising the cellular temperature. This is important because large temperature fluctuations affect the catalysts, or *enzymes*, on which all the body's chemical reactions depend. Enzymes, in fact, only work properly at about 37°c—that is, 98.6°F. Below this temperature, they act so slowly that the body becomes inactive. At temperatures much higher than 37°c., enzymes are destroyed and all bodily functions cease.

It often happens that so much heat is produced in the body that the excess cannot be removed by normal processes of radiation and conduction from the skin. The only way to remove this excess heat is by perspiration, where a watery secretion pours onto the skin's surface, and evaporates. During this change of state, latent heat is absorbed from the skin, and hence from the body—540 calories for every gram evaporated. The average sedentary man in a temperate climate loses about 500 cc. (about a pint) of water a day by perspiration, but in very hot climates the loss may rise to as much as 11,000 cc. This is a large water loss, but it is necessary

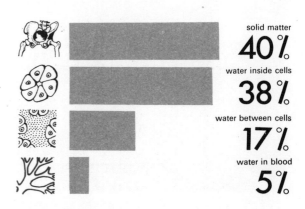

solid matter
40%

water inside cells
38%

water between cells
17%

water in blood
5%

Diagram above shows composition of average human in terms of water and solid matter. Man needs a daily water supply because there is a daily loss in the form of urine, sweat, etc., and because the body cannot store water as it does food.

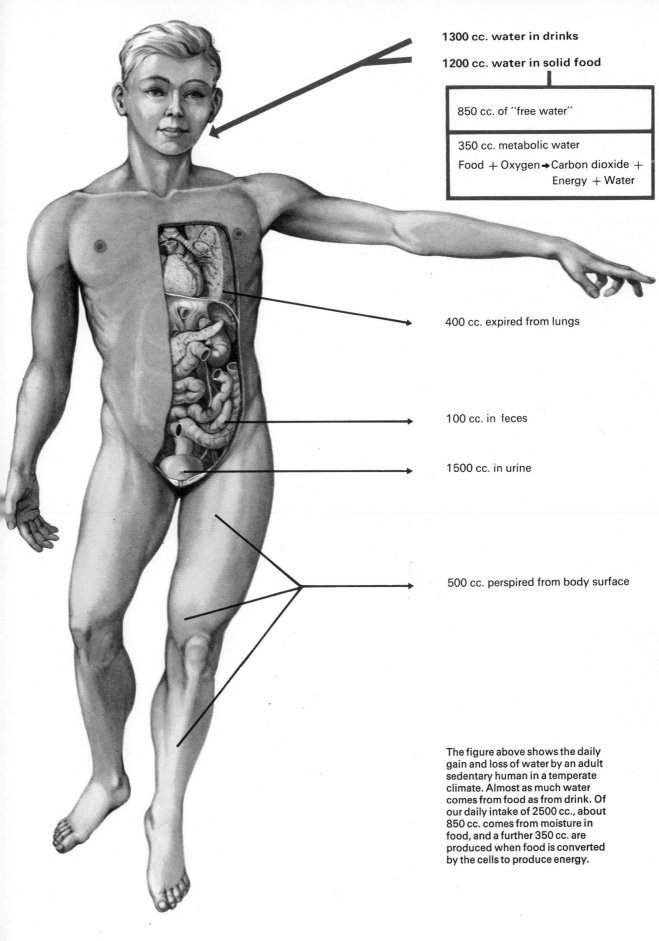

1300 cc. water in drinks

1200 cc. water in solid food

850 cc. of "free water"

350 cc. metabolic water
Food + Oxygen → Carbon dioxide + Energy + Water

400 cc. expired from lungs

100 cc. in feces

1500 cc. in urine

500 cc. perspired from body surface

The figure above shows the daily gain and loss of water by an adult sedentary human in a temperate climate. Almost as much water comes from food as from drink. Of our daily intake of 2500 cc., about 850 cc. comes from moisture in food, and a further 350 cc. are produced when food is converted by the cells to produce energy.

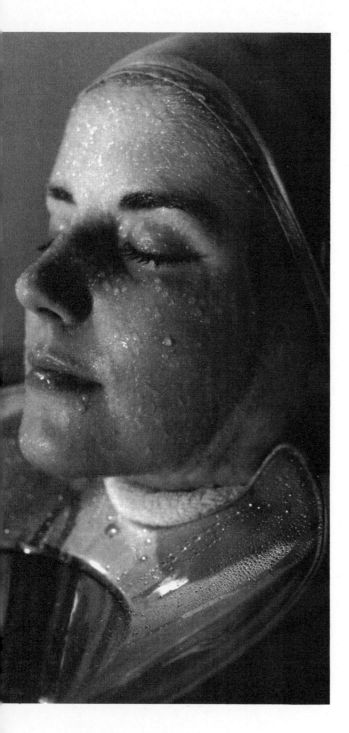

In temperate climates a human loses about 500 cc. (about 1 pint) a day through perspiration. In the tropics this loss may exceed 10 liters. Evaporation protects the body from serious or fatal over-heating. Hot humid climates are uncomfortable because sweat evaporates too slowly and forms droplets (photograph above).

to prevent a large rise in body temperature.

In temperate climates, the main loss of water from the body is by excretion, amounting to about 1500 cc. a day. In this process, the kidneys isolate waste substances from the blood and flush them out of the body in a watery urine. One waste substance is urea, which is produced from excess protein. But there are many other toxic or useless substances formed during metabolism, or eaten with solid food. The amount of water lost in the urine is partly related to the quantity of these excretory substances. A more important factor, though, is the relative amount of water and salt in the body. These concentrations must be kept within very narrow limits, otherwise cells dehydrate or burst. So when water or salt is present in excess, the urine is dilute; when too little is present, the urine is concentrated. All of which leads to an interesting point: Because regulating the concentration of body fluids is all-important, the body cannot store water to tide it over periods of drought in the same way that it can store solid food for periods of famine.

Our daily water loss thus averages 1500 cc. as urine, 500 cc. in perspiration, 400 cc. in exhaled air, and 100 cc. in the feces, totaling 2500 cc. Since a reduction in the body's water of anything over 10 per cent is fatal, roughly 2500 cc. must be taken into the body daily. We could, of course, drink this amount, but the average man drinks only about 1300 cc. The remaining water he obtains from food. A dry biscuit, for example, contains 5 per cent water, while fruit and vegetables are about 80 per cent water. This "free" water provides 850 cc. daily. The other 350 cc. are produced as a by-product of metabolism when food is burned to produce energy.

Although we drink only two pints daily, the domestic consumption of water in America may be over 180 gallons per head per day. Much of this is used for hygiene—baths, washing clothes, and flushing away waste into the sewers. The remaining water we use in various ways, such as watering the garden or cleaning the car. These are really luxuries when we compare today's life with that of 100 years ago.

If domestic water is man's most important need, water for crop irrigation comes a close second. In countries like Pakistan, the low rainfall supports only a few crops, and so irrigation is indispensable. Then there are areas like the southeast of England, where a large variety of crops can grow without irrigation, but grow much better with it. Here the purpose of irrigation is to add to what is already a reasonable rainfall in order to give a maximum crop yield. Unfortunately, the amount of water required for successful irrigation is enormous. Most of the water evaporates and transpires (p. 24) from soil and vegetation, and most of it cannot be re-used.

Lastly, large quantities of water are used in industry. Some industries are not essential for survival, but serve to provide man with amenities that are now considered one of the hallmarks of civilization. Other industries, of course, are essential—for instance, the manufacture of agricultural equipment or pipes for water supplies. The demands of industry and agriculture are such that the total consumption per head per day is now about 168 gallons in Europe, of which only about 48 gallons are supplied for use in the home. In America, consumption is about 1200 gallons per person per day.

It is one thing to state our requirements, and quite another to satisfy them. To do this successfully, we need, apart from money, a more detailed knowledge of the *hydrological cycle*—the process that involves the circulation and distribution of fresh water on earth. Before describing different aspects of this process in later chapters, we shall now give a brief outline of the cycle. The hydrological cycle begins and ends in the sea. From this there is no permanent deviation, but there are many different routes, or subcycles, that water can follow. Today, however, the cycle is not quite the same as it once was. Man removes large quantities of water from rivers and lakes and from underground, so that the old subcycles are complicated and new ones formed. It is thus no longer relevant to describe the hydrological cycle without describing the actions of man.

Although the hydrological cycle has no beginning or end, it is convenient to begin with evaporation from the sea. Evaporation continues as long as the air above the surface of the sea is not saturated with water vapor. Evaporation is quickest in the tropics, where the sun is most effective in warming the surface of the sea. Evaporation is also quickest when the air above the sea is warm, for the warmer the air, the more moisture it can hold.

The warm, moist air, being light, rises and is replaced by cold, dry air, which is heavy. As the air rises, it cools on meeting the cooler air above. It also cools as it expands at the lower atmospheric pressure. When the air temperature has fallen sufficiently, its vapor either condenses into droplets or freezes into ice crystals. These merge to form larger droplets and crystals until they are heavy enough to sink as rain, hail, or snow. Most of this precipitation falls into the sea, but one-eighth is swept inland by winds. In so doing, this maritime air meets considerable amounts of vapor that has evaporated from the land, and together they provide us with the precipitation that is our sole source of fresh water.

Not all precipitation on land benefits man. Some freezes on the icecaps of Greenland and Antarctica. This accumulation of solid water accounts for 70 per cent of all fresh water on earth. Another process over which we have little control is evaporation, which removes about 30 per cent of the precipitation over land. Evaporation occurs from rivers, lakes, and wet soil, and also from plant leaves, which intercept a large proportion of the rainfall. In countries with high temperatures, high wind speeds, or low air humidity, evaporation often exceeds rainfall. Thus the soil there dries up before rain has had time to promote plant growth.

After evaporation, the remaining water may infiltrate into the soil. In vegetated regions, much of this infiltrated water is absorbed by plant roots. It travels up the stems, and evaporates,

The kangaroo rat (above) lives in the desert and is an interesting example of an animal that never drinks, but obtains all its water from solid food.

23

or *transpires*, into the air through pores in the leaves. A tree may transpire about 60 gallons daily, very often removing all the infiltrated water. The combined effect of evaporation and transpiration, which we call *evapotranspiration*, can sometimes be reduced, for example, by covering water surfaces with substances that reduce evaporation. Deforestation also reduces evapotranspiration. But there are practical limits to how far we can reduce this process. One is that man needs plants to survive, and no plant is able to grow without transpiring.

The water that is not absorbed by plant roots slowly sinks through the fine network of channels in the soil. On its way, some is absorbed by clay particles, while some is held by surface tension as a thin film on the soil particles. This *soil moisture* evaporates very slowly into the soil channels, and soil particles remain moist for some time after rain stops.

When infiltration is heavy, some water may sink deeper into the soil until it reaches an impervious layer. The water accumulates above this layer and saturates overlying porous layers,

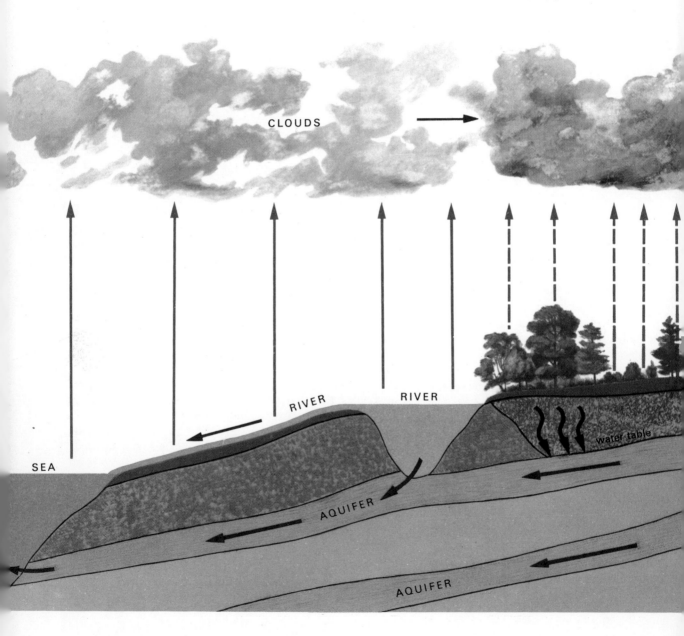

CLOUDS

RIVER

RIVER

water table

SEA

AQUIFER

AQUIFER

In the hydrological cycle (above), fresh water evaporates from oceans, and is blown by winds across land, where it precipitates as rain, snow, and hail. Well over half the precipitation evaporates soon after it falls to earth. The rest flows back to the oceans by way of rivers, lakes, and underground channels. Man obtains fresh water by trapping it at as many stages as possible before it escapes to the sea.

or *aquifers*. In regions of bad drainage, this *ground water* may remain static for thousands of years. In general, however, it slowly moves through the aquifers and sooner or later finds its way to the sea. A spring, for instance, may appear on the side of a hill where an aquifer is bared, and reach the sea by flowing into a neighboring stream. Ground water may enter rivers and lakes that cut through aquifers, thereby increasing their flow. The level of some rivers would fall seriously, were it not for this ground-water seepage.

The total amount of ground water far exceeds the water contained in rivers, lakes, and reservoirs. Ground water has always been, and still is, a cheap and vital source of water for public water supplies, irrigation, and industry. But much of it remains unusable because it is often heavily mineralized or too deep. Ground water also often moves very slowly through aquifers, and replenishments from precipitation may take anything from 1 to 50,000 years.

Until now, we have assumed that the soil absorbs all the precipitation that reaches it.

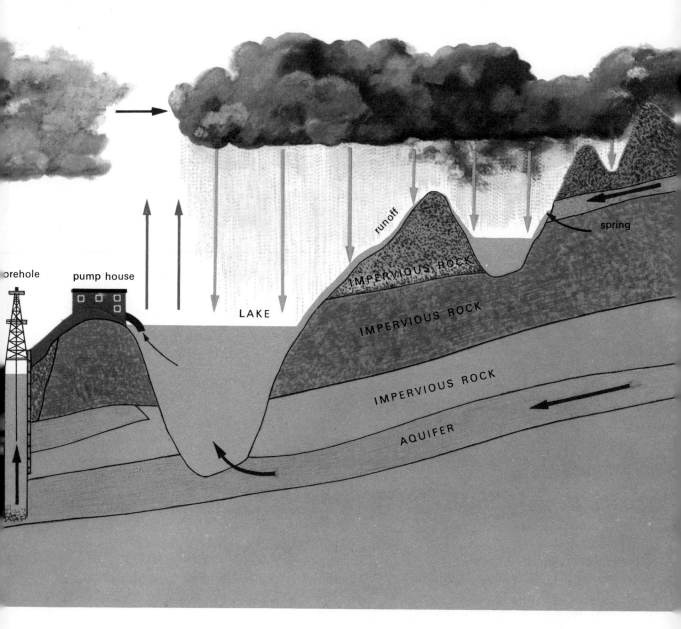

Evaporation from water surface

Evapotranspiration

Precipitation

Much of the land is relatively impermeable, however, and there are also times of year when normally permeable soils are so saturated with water that they are unable to absorb any more. In both these cases, precipitation forms *runoff*—that is, water that flows over the surface of the land in sheets or streams. Runoff finally enters the tributaries of small rivers, which in turn drain into larger rivers. Each continent has a few rivers whose tributaries drain immense areas of land. The Mississippi, for example, drains 40 per cent of the United States. A large part of South America is drained by the Amazon, and much of Africa by the Congo. Rivers provide a concentration of water that is invaluable to man, and are often the only source of water in areas of low rainfall, such as Egypt.

Also important as a source of water are lakes, which are formed when rivers flow into relatively impermeable basins. Most of this water occurs in a few large lakes, such as the Great Lakes of North America, Lake Baikal in Russia, Lakes Tanganyika and Nyasa in Africa. Lakes store much of the surplus runoff during periods of heavy rainfall. This stored water then helps to increase the outgoing river level during periods of low rainfall. Not only does this increase the amount of water that man can remove from rivers in drought, but it also reduces the intensity of river floods.

In many areas, engineers have investigated the relationships between rivers, lakes, ground water, and evapotranspiration. Mathematicians, meanwhile, have tried to discover the rules that govern the behavior of these different parts of the hydrological cycle. But the results of detailed research in one region cannot necessarily be applied to another, because each area is a unique part of the hydrological cycle. Even a small country like England consists of many areas with different rainfalls and amounts of ground and surface water. To understand fully the distribution and behavior of water in a particular area therefore requires a thorough knowledge of the principles of hydrology, together with a careful study of local conditions.

One striking fact that emerges from our discussion of the hydrological cycle is that the water we use and drink has passed through many different subcycles over a period of many thousands of years. A drop of water may travel from the sea, across land, and back to the sea again, without ever falling to earth. Yet the following week the same drop may take a different route, to be locked for centuries in Antarctic ice. Vapor from the sea may be swept across a mountain range, condense as rain, and fall into the headwaters of a river. From here, it may flow down to the sea, or it may seep through the riverbed to form ground water. If it is pumped out of the river or ground for irrigation, it may end up as the moisture content of a grain of corn, and be eaten. If this same water then leaves the body in the urine, it becomes part of a sewage that discharges back into the river. Man obtains water by intercepting these subcycles at various stages, but this does not always produce enough water. The only answer for some parts of the world is to bypass all these subcycles by going directly to the sea for fresh water, an expensive method that we shall examine in later chapters.

Left: Diagram shows the main rivers and tributaries of North America. Most river water comes from runoff—water that flows over the land surface. A smaller proportion derives from the infiltration of ground water through the riverbed. Unfortunately, most river water escapes to the sea before it can be used, although the amount is being reduced by trapping it in reservoirs.

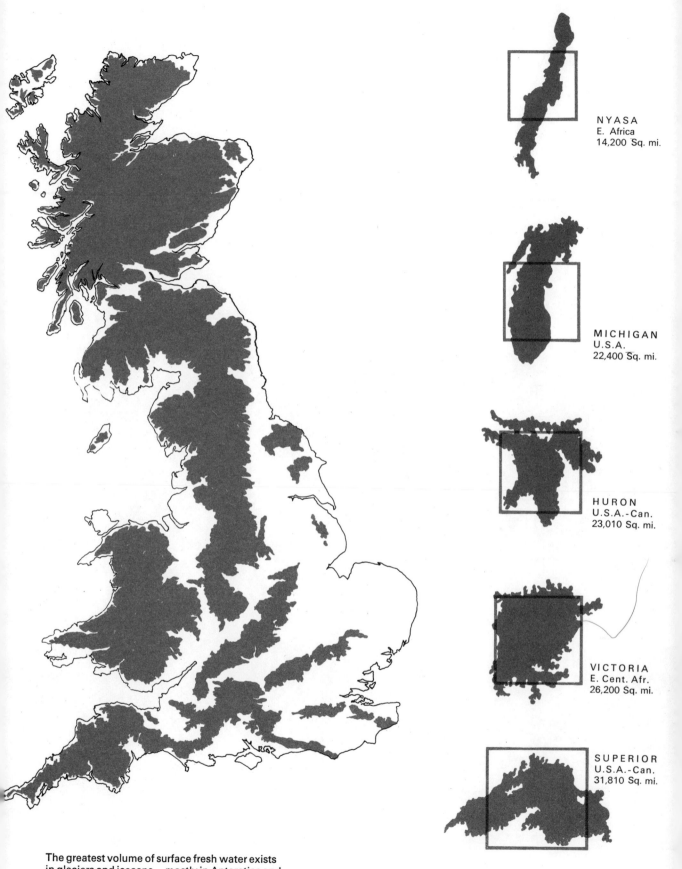

NYASA
E. Africa
14,200 Sq. mi.

MICHIGAN
U.S.A.
22,400 Sq. mi.

HURON
U.S.A.-Can.
23,010 Sq. mi.

VICTORIA
E. Cent. Afr.
26,200 Sq. mi.

SUPERIOR
U.S.A.-Can.
31,810 Sq. mi.

The greatest volume of surface fresh water exists
in glaciers and icecaps—mostly in Antarctica and
Greenland—but is useless as a large source of fresh
water. If all this ice melted, the sea level would
rise and flood vast areas of land around the world.
Only the brown areas in the above map of Britain would
remain uncovered.

Lakes contain about four times
more water than rivers. Above:
Five of the largest lakes—the
squares denote their relative areas.

3 No Water Without Life

In the above cartoon of 1858, Father Thames presents his children to the city of London, symbolizing the state of the river at this time and the major diseases that it carried. These diseases declined only when treatment of Thames water was introduced.

Water, as we have seen, is an essential part of all living matter. So it is not surprising that water should also be an ideal home for living matter. Wherever there are rivers, lakes, reservoirs, and ponds, there is some form of life. Well-water may also contain organisms, but in most water deep underground, life is impossible for lack of nutrients, oxygen, or light.

No organism can live without dissolved salts. It needs these to build up its protoplasm, the essential substance of plant and animal cells. Plants absorb salts directly from the water, while animals obtain salts by eating either plants or other animals. Since fresh water is usually moving, it has little time to accumulate salts. The sea, however, has no outlet, and therefore accumulates salts that have been washed down from the land for millions of years. Fresh water seldom supports a plant and animal population to the same extent as the sea.

Nevertheless, lakes and rivers do support a considerable number of organisms, mainly in the top 10 to 20 feet, which is the depth to which light penetrates. Here microscopic plants, called phytoplankton, use light for *photosynthesis*, the process by which plants convert chemical substances into life-supporting materials. These phytoplankton thus provide food for tiny animals, which in turn are eaten by larger ones. At the other extreme, fresh water may contain large water plants, which in excess choke lakes and rivers. They may also contain large animals, such as the hippopotamus. In rivers, most of this life occurs in the slow-moving reaches, in deltas, and in coastal plains, where the river nears its end and therefore has the highest concentration of salts. Also, the flow is not as fast as upstream, so there is a better foothold for organisms.

Much of this life in fresh water is harmless, and some is beneficial. But in water there also lurk organisms, invisible to the naked eye, that have caused more sickness and death than all the wars in history. These are the *pathogenic* bacteria, viruses, and protozoa. We can show the impact of these organisms by taking the city of London as an example, because it was one of the first cities in the nineteenth century in which a rapidly expanding population led to serious trouble. Between 1831 and 1893, for example, London suffered badly from nation-wide cholera epidemics that claimed 50,000 victims—almost

as many civilians as died in Britain during the air raids of World War II.

At the beginning of the nineteenth century, the expectation of life was only 30 years. This was largely due to the effect of several water-borne diseases, such as typhoid, cholera, dysentery (amoebic and bacillary), virus jaundice, and gastroenteritis. It took a long time for people to realize that the cause of these diseases was bad sanitation and infected water. Very few people had toilets, and human waste was discharged into ditches and cesspools. This was quite a good method of sewage disposal for small villages, but was not suitable for large cities like London, which drew much of its water from wells. When large amounts of sewage seeped through the ground, the pathogenic bacteria in it sometimes leaked through cracks in wells to infect the water. Thus one infected person spread disease to hundreds of others.

Up to 1815 it was a penal offense to discharge human waste into the Thames River, then the main source of domestic water. But as toilets became more common, a network of sewers was built, which inevitably ran downhill to the river. The large quantity of sewage that now poured into the Thames meant that London's main water source became dangerous to health, in addition to the already contaminated wells. People continued to take water from the tidal reaches of the Thames, often from near sewer outlets. The old complaints persisted, especially during hot weather when bacteria thrive best. Ironically, the efforts to improve sanitation, and thus health, by providing extensive sewers defeated its own purpose.

In 1852 the first real move to improve the water supply was made in London by passing the Metropolis Water Act. Water companies were obliged to remove their river intakes out of the tidal zone of the Thames, to above the first lock at Teddington, and therefore out of reach of London's sewage. The Act also ordered the filtration of all river-derived water. The engineer James Simpson had introduced an experimental slow sand filter at Chelsea in 1829. The subsequent decline in the cholera rate in this area proved it a great success. Yet filtration did not become common until after 1866. Meanwhile, Dr. John Snow showed by careful observation that many diseases were not air-borne, as was generally believed, but water-borne. Then came the discovery of bacteria, and the story of water-borne disease was nearly complete. In 1885, the Water Board of London began a routine bacteriological check of all river water, but many years elapsed before bacteriological checks were kept on all rivers.

In spite of filtration, and siting the water intakes at less polluted parts of the river, water-borne disease persisted until the early 1900's. Various improvements took time, and did not keep pace with the rapidly increasing population. The advent of safe water only came with the widespread application of *chlorination* in the 1930's (a process first applied in 1897). Not only do tiny amounts of chlorine destroy up to 99.95 per cent of all intestinal bacteria, but chlorine can be added to water just before it enters the mains. So whatever pathogens may have survived filtration are destroyed in the end. During this century, there have been sporadic outbreaks of typhoid due to the lack of chlorination, and water authorities finally realized that the process must never be omitted.

In order to eradicate disease, water must not only be sterile, but should be supplied to every house in sufficient quantity. Up to the middle 1800's, few of the houses in large cities had a piped water supply, and then only for a few hours each week. The poor often begged water from the rich, and stored it in vessels, where it was liable to contamination. But when houses began to received piped water, people were able to wash themselves regularly as well as their clothes and premises, thus removing disease-producing parasites such as lice. More important still, people began to wash their hands, so that intestinal pathogens were prevented from spreading to food and other people by contact.

In many underdeveloped countries, the prevalence of water-borne disease is still as it was in England 100 years ago. In some of these countries, intestinal disease is still one of the prime causes of infant mortality. As there is no efficient medical treatment, the only answer is a safe water supply. But it is very difficult to convince people of the benefits of hygiene, especially where water is concerned. And even when they are convinced they do not always have the money to install a safe water supply.

There are many diseases in hot climates that are not caused by bad sanitation, but are simply due to the *presence* of water. Canals, marshes, cisterns, water barrels, and holes in trees, all provide breeding places for the young stages of mosquitoes that transmit malaria, yellow fever, and dengue fever. Water also supports several worms and flukes that infect men and cattle. Of particular importance is the fluke *Bilharzia* (*Schistosoma*), which in the tropics and sub-tropics causes great suffering to over 200 million people. When a person comes in contact with infected water, the parasite enters the skin and breeds inside the body. The eggs of the parasite pass back into the water with human excreta, and the offspring then become parasitic on snails. From there, hundreds of new parasites later emerge to infect more people. In many areas, irrigation has led to a sharp rise in this disease, largely defeating efforts to improve health by increased food production. In Egypt and the Sudan, irrigation from storing the Nile flood-water increased bilharziasis to a level where, in some areas, 80 per cent of the population were infected.

Some countries are beginning to learn that water projects must be designed to prevent parasites from becoming established. Otherwise, people must be prepared for the large cost of killing them by the continual application of selective poisons. At present, the health of a large proportion of the population in many tropical areas is so undermined that their low production and standards of living are hardly surprising. The natives are not willfully idle, but simply miserable and weakened by parasites.

We now move on to the forms of life that do not cause disease but instead give trouble to water authorities. Problems begin as soon as water enters the storage reservoir. Although many bacteria die in static water, it is an ideal habitat for algae—simple plant forms that often appear as scum on the water's surface. At certain times of the year, algae may reproduce explosively, especially when polluted river water overloads the reservoirs with nutrient salts. Algae then block the reservoir filters or slow sand filter beds. Some algae also impart to water a taste that is sometimes difficult to remove. Others produce substances that are inoffensive except in certain industries, such as those producing soft drinks.

Even after water has left the waterworks it may be contaminated by other forms of life that establish themselves in the water mains. In the past, these organisms were quite a problem. In 1886, for example, the pipe network in Hamburg, Germany, became blocked with eels, sponges, shrimps, water lice, and worms. Although harmless enough, these were unsavory things to emerge from the faucet. Today, filtration is always practiced in efficient waterworks, so that the presence of large organisms in the pipes is rare, but this is not so for microorganisms. However efficient the filtration, some dissolved organic matter may enter the pipes to provide food for these microorganisms. If the water also contains dissolved iron salts, brownish slimes are produced by iron bacteria, which on decay may give water an unpleasant color and taste. Iron bacteria also cause lumps of encrusted rust inside pipes, reducing the water flow by as much as 75 per cent. These lumps of rust may also harbor larger organisms.

During the last 50 years, waterweeds have gained a strong foothold in many parts of the world. The most troublesome weeds are those that become established in countries far away from their native haunt. One way in which this happens is when foreign aquarium plants are imported with tropical fish and are then emptied into streams. Rooted weeds establish themselves in the slow-moving parts of rivers, impede the current, and therefore cause more silt to accumulate around their stems, providing anchorage for new weeds. The main offenders are the floating weeds, especially the South American water hyacinth. In only four months, a couple of parent plants multiply to over a thousand, creating vast, interlocked mats three-feet thick.

Above: The Congo River blocked by South American water hyacinth. Waterweeds may multiply like this when they accidentally reach rivers far from their native region. Attempts are being made to use the manatee (top) to clear canals in Florida of these weeds.

In 1890 several states of the American South were infested by the water hyacinth. The same problem had developed by 1895 in Australia, in India by 1902, and in 1000 miles of the Congo River by 1952. By 1960, 600 miles of the White Nile were covered, as far as the Jebel Awlia Dam near Khartoum. Navigation almost came to a stop. Irrigation pumps were blocked, and fishermen were unable to wade for fish, many of which had already died through deoxygenation of the water. Furthermore, the large amount of water lost by plant transpiration (p. 24) only made matters worse in an area where already half the original Nile flow is lost by evaporation.

Complete eradication of the water hyacinth is unlikely, for the seeds can lie dormant for several years, and are very resistant. With sufficient money, it is possible to control the plant, as is done in the southern United States, but money on a large scale is seldom available for underdeveloped countries. At the Jebel Awlia Dam, for instance, $1.4 million are spent annually in just keeping part of the White Nile navigable and in preventing fragments of the plant from passing downstream, where there is a danger of obstructing the canals. Dragging the mats out of the water is extremely difficult and expensive, as is spraying with herbicides such as 2,4-D. Aerial spraying, often the most economical method, is not always feasible, because crops such as cotton are particularly susceptible to 2,4-D. The possibility of biological control—that is, controlling the unwanted plant by introducing some natural enemy—is being examined.

Another troublesome floating plant is the *water fern*. Also a native of South America, the plant has spread to several parts of the world, where it often interferes with irrigation projects. Over a period of 12 years, the plant has covered 22,000 acres of Ceylon's rice fields. In 1962, 400 square miles of Africa's Lake Kariba were covered, creating a mat that was so dense that it provided anchorage for as many as 40 different rooted plants. Now only 10 per cent of the lake is covered, and fortunately the prevailing winds drift the mats away from the grids of the turbine intakes at the Kariba Dam.

Some fresh-water organisms, of course, are invaluable, especially in the yearly disposal of hundreds of thousands of tons of sewage. If this waste accumulated, there would be a very high disease rate, quite apart from its offensiveness. As it is, microorganisms find in sewage a rich source of nutrients and energy, and break it down into harmless substances. This natural process of purification occurs in rivers, lakes, and in the soil. Microorganisms are also used in sewage works (Chapter 10) and to treat industrial organic waste.

Microorganisms are also sometimes used for treating domestic water, in combination with slow sand filter beds (p. 136). After filtration has proceeded for some time, a jellylike film appears on the surface of the sand, formed by bacteria and algae. These are followed later by bacteria below the surface that surround each sand particle with a similar film. Both these films form an extremely efficient filter for small suspended solids and bacteria. But the action is more than a straining process. It is also a chemical reaction called oxidation, or oxygenation—a change like that produced by combining with oxygen. The organisms oxidize organic matter to inorganic compounds, precipitate iron salts, and retain the copper salts that are used to destroy algae in storage reservoirs. Also, the algae oxygenate the water, hastening the oxidation of harmful substances. The oxygenation also prevents anaerobic bacteria (those able to live in the absence of free oxygen) from flourishing deep down in the filter bed.

Finally, there are the fish that spend part or all of their lives in fresh water. For people who cannot obtain enough protein from meat and dairy produce, fish may be often the only source. In the Far East, fish are farmed in tanks, and also in flooded paddy fields. In affluent countries, fresh-water fish are not so important as a source of protein, but salmon and trout are still luxury dishes. These edible fish, and many others, have disappeared from many rivers because of pollution, which either deprives the water of oxygen, or directly poisons the fish. Open-air recreations, however, such as fishing, are becoming ever more important as man seeks to escape from the mechanization of city life. For all of the above reasons and more, it has become a moral responsibility of local authorities, industry, and all people to do everything in their power to prevent the pollution of rivers.

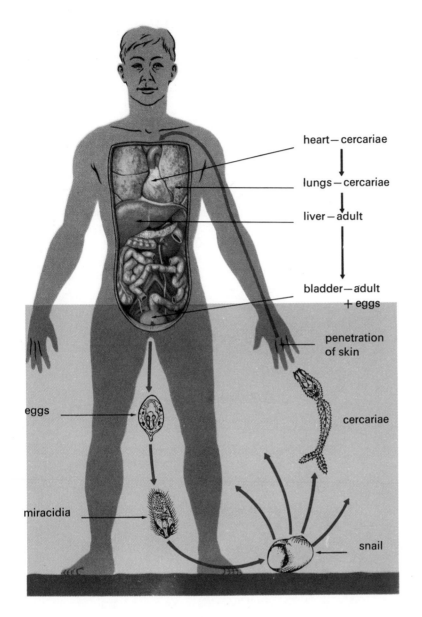

heart — cercariae

↓

lungs — cercariae

↓

liver — adult

↓

bladder — adult
+ eggs

penetration
of skin

eggs

miracidia

cercariae

snail

Left: Life cycle of *Schistosoma haematobium*—one of many water-borne parasites that undermine physical and mental health in many underdeveloped countries. Drinking, fishing, washing, and working on irrigated land may lead to schistosomiasis (bilharziasis). The cercariae (larval form) penetrate the skin, especially of the hands, feet, and lining of the mouth. After passing through heart and lungs, cercariae end up in the liver, and become adult flukes, or "worms." Flukes then travel to veins of bladder wall, and may produce eggs for up to 40 years. Eggs bore through bladder wall with aid of spines and digestive juices, and it is this stage that damages the body most. After eggs leave body in the urine, they hatch into miracidia, another stage of the parasite, that then penetrate a water snail. Here they turn into other stages, and finally into thousands of cercariae, and the cycle begins again. Thus each egg released by urinating into water produces thousands of cercariae, each of which can infect another person.

Below: This man working on irrigated land is in danger of infection through his bare hands and feet. Irrigation has led to an increase in schistosomiasis.

Below left: Map shows distribution of the three species of Schistosoma, which together afflict over 200 million people.

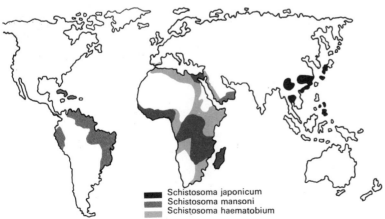

■ Schistosoma japonicum
■ Schistosoma mansoni
■ Schistosoma haematobium

4 Man's Water Requirements

About 10,000 years ago, most of the earth's inhabitants were nomads who roamed in the neighborhood of rivers and lakes. These provided not only drinking water but also grazing along their banks. Several thousand years later, many people began to change their way of life: They started to live in settled communities. In this new way of life, man's basic requirements for food and water remained the same, but the means by which he obtained them had to change. First, he had to draw water continually from the same place. Second, to provide enough food for a settled population, he had to grow and tend crops. In other words, he started to farm. To do this successfully, he often had to supplement a scanty rainfall with river water, and so he began to work out the basic principles of irrigation.

In some parts of the world, man has never moved beyond these first simple methods of water supply and irrigation. But in other parts, there grew up around 3000 B.C. a series of elaborate civilizations whose domestic and agricultural use of water was often more advanced than that of many developing parts of the world today. These civilizations evolved in areas of very low rainfall—specifically, in the valleys of the Tigris, Euphrates, Indus, Nile, and Yellow rivers. These rivers provided irrigation either by the natural flooding of the land, or by supplying water to man-made canals. Since seasonal floods occurred about once a year, at least one crop a year was harvested. Sometimes, however, the floods were so big that the crops were ruined. The peoples of these river valleys were compelled to use great ingenuity to overcome the double problem of obtaining enough water for domestic and agricultural use, and of preventing excessive flooding of the land.

After 3000 B.C. water began to be used in quite sophisticated ways—for baths, for toilets, and for irrigating pleasure gardens, such as the famous hanging gardens of Babylon. The bathrooms and toilets of Mesopotamia certainly made the fullest use of water, and waste water ran into brick-vaulted sewers under the streets. Later, as the population increased, armies of slaves toiled to provide water in even greater quantities. Wells were dug to supply clean drinking water. Covered cisterns were built in cities to store water for use during dry spells. And canals were dug to bring water from further afield, like the 50-mile canal that brought upland water to Nineveh. The canals were not made simply by digging trenches in the crude manner of the eighteenth century in Europe, but were carefully constructed of stone or brick, and waterproofed with bitumen, a kind of asphalt. It was as if life in areas of low rainfall inspired these ancient peoples to devise the most ingenious ways of exploiting water. We see the same determination today in the arid areas of Israel and in the southwestern United States.

Yet while these ancient civilizations developed their water supplies, they also warred with one another. Gradually the water systems that had taken so much time and knowledge to construct crumbled into ruin. After the fall of the Roman Empire, the dark age of water began. If there were communities that used water to the full, they were few and far between. It was not, in fact, until the late nineteenth century that man once more reached the standard of water use set some 5000 years before.

When, in the nineteenth century, men began to build new water systems, it was not on the sites of the old eastern civilizations. The scene shifts mainly to Western Europe and America. Here the water engineers' problems were intensified by the rapid growth in population that followed the Industrial Revolution. Before, most people lived in villages and small towns, where

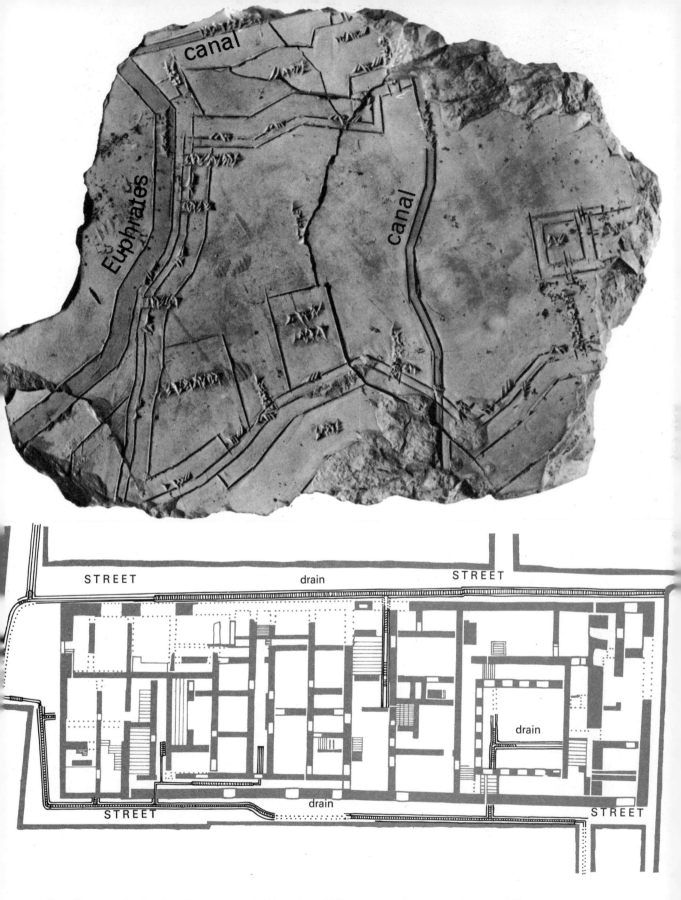

Top: Photograph of a clay tablet engraved with a plan of Nippur, an ancient cultural center of Mesopotamia. The plan, probably the oldest known of a city, shows the use of canals leading from the Euphrates. Bottom: Plan of Mohenjo-Daro, a city that flourished near the Indus River around 2500 B.C. The inhabitants had a high standard of hygiene: Each house had its bathroom and toilet from which waste was flushed by water into chutes that led to covered street drains or sewers.

there was little danger of depleting or polluting water sources. But now large populations were mainly concentrated in industrial cities, where water was often in short supply or polluted. In spite of the comparatively heavy rainfall in many parts of Europe and America, the new cities began to run short of water. Many people had to be content with a spasmodic supply, of a quality that some ancient peoples would not have tolerated.

The rapidly increasing population also meant that, after the nineteenth century, communities were no longer free to move to areas with better water resources. When, for example, the Euphrates and Tigris rivers changed their courses, new cities were built on different sites. This is obviously impossible today, for not only are most potential new sites already occupied, but our cities are too large and complex to abandon. We are therefore confronted with the problem of conveying large quantities of water to already existing cities, often for hundreds of miles, and of transporting water to buildings through a pipe network.

Only 400 million of the 2400 million people living in Africa, Latin America, and Asia receive piped water. Most of this piped supply ends in a public outlet at the end of the street, and is by no means constant. In countries with a high standard of living, most houses receive piped water, and also possess sinks, toilets, and baths. But these amenities, which we now take for granted, are very recent innovations. A century ago a single outdoor faucet supplied a whole street, and as recently as 1920 only one-third of the houses in Britain had a toilet.

Today, we expect a very high standard from our water supplies. Our first requirement is *quality*—that is, water should be palatable, oxygenated, colorless, odorless, and free from organisms and harmful salts. Next in importance after quality is *quantity*. To stress the inconvenience caused by a prolonged reduction in supply, we must first consider a few figures for water consumption in the home. For a reasonably well-off British citizen, the average *daily* consumption of water in gallons can be broken down approximately in the following way: drinks, .6; flushing toilets, 12; personal washing and cleaning teeth, 9.6; waiting for water to run hot, 4.8; baths (two a week), 7.2; cooking and washing dishes, 6; cleaning house, 1.2; washing clothes, 4.8; cleaning car, .6. This amounts to a daily total of about 47 gallons.

These figures refer only to the actual *use* of water in the home. The really significant figure, however, is the amount actually entering the mains from the treatment works. This always exceeds the amount actually used, because it includes leakage from pipes and from domestic plumbing fixtures which totals about 9.6 gallons per head per day (ghd) in efficiently run waterworks. In future chapters when we talk about the *consumption* of piped water, we include its

Left: One of many family swimming pools that now abound in California. Such water-consuming activities help to make California's domestic consumption one of the highest in the world.

Right: These firemen are able to fight this typical fire only because there is a large supply of mains water. Even so, fire caused about $1.5 billion worth of damage in the United States in 1965.

use by the consumer as well as leakage. In all of Britain, the total consumption from the mains is 66 ghd. Of that, 40 gal. are for the domestic consumer and 26 gal. for industry. But in the next three decades this is likely to reach 120 ghd, a figure already approached in Stockholm, Berlin, Moscow, Paris, and Rome.

In many parts of the United States, the domestic consumption exceeds 180 ghd. In some areas this figure is partly due to excessive waste, either by the consumer or by leakage from pipes. Americans also make more demands on their supply than do Europeans. Air conditioning consumes large amounts of water; automatic washing machines swallow 36 gallons per wash; garbage grinders require water to dispose of kitchen waste; toilets use 7.2 gallons per flush compared with 2.4 in England. The heaviest consumers in America are perhaps located in the arid parts of California, where water has become a status symbol. Here we find lush gardens, including lawns with built-in sprinklers and exotic swimming pools. Many would label these extravagant luxuries, but Californians pay for the water they use by meter. Thus, it seems that they should be free to use as much as they can afford, provided they do not deprive others in need. This argument, of course, applies only where the water sources are able to cope with such high demands. If they run dry, then desalination (p. 145) may be the only alternative.

Our third requirement of a domestic supply is that water should be provided *continously*, and at a high enough *pressure* (about 40 lb. per sq. in.) to reach with ease the top floor of an average house. Owners of tall buildings must fix booster pumps to lift water to the upper floors. A continuous water supply at high pressure is also essential for fire-fighting, although fire engines also have booster pumps. Access to water for fighting fires is particularly important in cities, where one fire may easily spread to adjacent buildings. Water authorities therefore install fire hydrants at intervals along streets so that any fire can be quickly hosed with water from the mains.

Enough water to sweep waste matter along the sewers is essential to prevent filth and disease. Some of this transport water enters sewers from toilets, sinks, baths, and some from factories. A large amount of rain may also enter many sewers via street drains. Sometimes, during severe drought, there is not enough water for the transport of sewage. When this happened in Western Europe during the drought of 1921 and in New York in 1965, chemical deodorizers had to be injected into the sewers at great expense.

We now move on to the water requirements of industry, which in a country like Britain account for about 40 per cent of the total water consumption from water authorities. Nearly two-thirds of industrial water is used for cooling and condensing. One ton of steel requires between

12,000 and 60,000 gallons for its manufacture; some chemical products may need 48,000 gallons per ton. The textile and paper industries are also large consumers, needing about 26,000 gallons for one ton of product. Water is often an ingredient in food-making. For example, $\frac{1}{2}$ lb. of water is added to every 1 lb. of flour to make bread. All these types of industry are necessary for the kind of civilization that we have chosen for ourselves. In the future there will be even heavier demands on the water supply as industrialization and population increase.

In times of drought, or when the river level is low, the consumption by industry sometimes affects the domestic supply of water. All that is required of industry is to reduce water waste to a minimum and to return what is left to the river in a fit state for use by other consumers. A steelworks may use 36 million gallons per day (mgd), and return it in a re-usable condition. Or it may use only 1 mgd 36 times over, by which time it may be so contaminated that it requires special treatment before discharge into the river. In Europe and America increasingly severe regulations are being drawn up and slowly put into effect, which force industry both to re-use water and to purify its effluents—that is, any part that is returned to water system.

Most industries require good quality water, but their standards are often different from those of the domestic consumer. The householder wants water free from harmful organisms. Industry is more concerned with its mineral content. Sometimes, as in laundries, only a few minerals need be removed, which is simply done by a water softener. Water used in high-pressure boilers, however, must be almost completely demineralized. Otherwise heat and evaporation will precipitate and concentrate salts into a thick insulating scale in boilers and pipes. This scale is expensive to remove. It also seriously reduces the conductivity of heat-transferring surfaces and raises the temperature of the metal to a level where it may deteriorate. In the pharmaceutical industry, water is completely demineralized by treble distillation.

In the manufacture of food and drinks, water must be free of organisms and also of certain minerals and organic compounds. These substances, which are sometimes present in the domestic water supply, may not be noticed in a glass of water. But when incorporated into food and drink, they may produce turbidity and unwanted tastes and odors.

In many parts of the world, enormous quantities of water are needed for irrigation. In fact, most of the world's food is produced in those regions that are already irrigated. Many parts of the world need irrigation to prevent a small population from starving. There are parts of Africa, for example, that have no rain for several years. Botswana, for instance, entered its fifth year of drought in 1966. Without water, harvests fail, cattle die by the thousand, and children die of malnutrition, or from pneumonia and enteritis brought on by lack of food.

Other areas of low rainfall, such as the valleys of the Nile, Tigris, and Indus, at least have the benefit of river water. Natural flooding of the land, or the deliberate diversion of water through canals, enables crops to be sown, harvested, and stored for the dry season. And because the annual peak river flow is fairly reliable, there is enough water for a large population to live at a low standard. The achievement of a *high* standard of living in areas of low rainfall, however, requires more than just cheap labor. It needs special technical knowledge, and enough money, carefully applied, to develop and maintain water storage and irrigation systems. With the aid of these, apparent miracles can be performed, as can be seen in California and in Israel.

Many parts of the world are now short of food because their populations have grown too large to be fed by locally grown crops. The situation is different in well-developed countries with a high rainfall, where large populations are fed by using irrigation to produce a *maximum* crop yield. We are therefore faced with the possibility that, as populations increase, not only may supplies of fresh water become insufficient, but also food supplies may run short. This is an insuperable problem in places where populations and water consumption are increasing at the rate of more than 5 per cent a year. Industry and the domestic consumer may have enough water for a long time to come. But it is unlikely that there will ever be enough water to irrigate more than a small fraction of the earth's surface, even if all the present water sources were economically exploited. The amount of water needed for irrigation is enormous—a square mile of crop-land lacking 12 inches of rain would need 209 million gallons. To make matters worse, most of it cannot be re-used because it is lost by evapotranspiration, by sinking into the ground, or by becoming part of the crop itself.

So far we have concentrated mainly on the problems of supplying enough water. But the fact that water is rarely present in the right quantity, at the right time, and at the right place may also result in there being far too much. Most countries have suffered from floods that have destroyed human and animal life, property, and crops. The control of floods, however, is often more difficult than providing a secure water supply. In the past, many cities developed along the fertile plains of large rivers, which conveniently afforded the benefits of a water supply, cheap navigation, and a means of removing sewage. There are no longer such compelling reasons for building on flood plains, yet the cities that remain are expanding. Thus, when flooding does occur the damage is correspondingly greater. In America well over $300 million are spent each year to make it profitable to continue living on flood plains. But in other areas serious floods are so rare that it would be uneconomic to spend large sums to prevent them. When, for instance, the Thames flooded parts of London in December 1965, the small damage caused was tolerated because the cost of prevention would have exceeded the cost of repair.

Protection must be provided from the catastrophic flood, however. One method of control, used in the Tennessee Valley Authority (p. 89), is to store floodwater in reservoirs. The water is then allowed to flow gradually downstream over a long period of time. Another method, adopted on the lower Mississippi, is to cut canals across river loops, which increases the river's gradient so that more water flows in a given time. By far the commonest device is to enclose the river with walls (called *levees* or *dikes*) high enough to prevent water overflowing. The lower Mississippi has over 2500 miles of these walls, 30 feet high in places. But like many rivers that carry high seasonal floodwaters, the bed of the Mississippi silts up, and the walls have to be continually raised. It is for this reason that the city of New Orleans, for example, lies below river level.

This laundry (left) uses about 54,000 gallons of water per day, and all of it is treated to remove the salts that produce hardness. Softening saves soap and protects fabrics. The photograph above shows a section of pipe lined with scale due to the use of hot, hard water. To prevent this, industry must demineralize water almost completely.

If we have sometimes seemed to overemphasize economics, it is because the principal object of any water supply system is to secure water at the lowest possible cost. The price we pay for water is really very low considering the enormous cost of dams, reservoirs, treatment works, and pipelines. The main reason for the low cost of water is our willingness to share its benefits with others. The expense of individual projects for each house or small community would be prohibitive. Also we owe a great deal to technological improvements, notably the development of pipes that leak less and last longer. Even so, we must be prepared to pay more in the future.

Expanding populations require more water, and since most of the near sources are fully exploited, this will mean tapping distant sources, at considerable expense. In many places, the domestic metering of water would discourage waste. It is estimated, for example, that metering the domestic supply in New York would reduce consumption by 40 per cent. But many city dwellers want it both ways—to continue their large consumption, and still pay low bills. The success of future water supplies thus not only depends on the application of new techniques. It also relies on educating the public to appreciate the value and the cost of water, which at present they take too much for granted.

These photographs express the water situation for most of the world—either too much or too little. Yearly floods cause extensive damage on the Mississippi (below). For the United States as a whole, floods caused $700 million worth of damage in 1965.

Right: An Indian lies on his *charpoy* waiting for the monsoon rains while his wife returns from a long trek with a jar of water. Until the rains come, no grain can be sown, and even then, as in 1965, insufficient rain may result in famine.

5   Water Supply

Having discussed various water requirements, we now investigate how these are met. Any water-supply system involves taking water from its source, treating it, and distributing it to the consumer. How this is done varies from one area to another, so we start by examining the various methods available at present and the principles they involve. Then we discuss in detail the water supply in various parts of the world so as to cover the most common types of system.

The *sources* of water today are much the same as they were thousands of years ago. We still rely mainly on rivers, lakes, springs, and wells, but we now exploit them more extensively. After the invention of the steam engine in the early eighteenth century, and the subsequent development of power-driven drills and pumps, it became possible to drill deep boreholes and to lift water from depths of over 1000 feet. We have increased the storage of natural lakes by building dams, and have created new reservoirs by damming water in river valleys. Where there is no natural fresh-water source, a few places—such as Kuwait on the Persian Gulf—desalinate sea water.

Choosing a source is not easy, and exploiting it is a very complex procedure. Many mistakes have been made in the past. Wells have been dug into brine-fields (water saturated with salt), and dams built on shaky foundations. If possible, a source should fulfill three conditions: It should be as near as possible to the population in need (the supply area); the water should be available in sufficient quantity; and it should not contain high concentrations of objectionable salts or be too polluted.

A common source is the large river. When clean and near to the area of supply, a river is especially economical because it avoids the great expense of building distant reservoirs and aqueducts. Unfortunately, the large amounts of water that many rivers yield for much of the year often dwindle to a trickle in the dry season, just when the demand is greatest. Rivers also carry silt, and are a convenient flushing system for municipal sewage and a convenient disposer of industrial effluent. Thus river water needs thorough treatment. But recent developments in water treatment have made it possible to use polluted river water that would not have been possible before.

Natural lakes, such as the Great Lakes, often provide a good local, reliable supply to their nearby cities. But lakes, like rivers, are liable to be heavily polluted by the very people they are intended to serve. This experience is not met with so much in isolated lakes and reservoirs far from the area of supply. In these relatively unpopulated areas of runoff—called *catchment areas*, *basins*, or *watersheds*—streams carry suspended matter into the lake or reservoir. There it slowly falls to the bottom, most of the bacteria die, and the water becomes relatively clean. If such a source is high up in the hills, its water can flow to the cities under gravity, thus saving pumping costs. Unlike rivers, lakes and reservoirs are more able to store floodwaters, which may be slowly drawn upon during dry periods. But like all sources, lakes and reservoirs have drawbacks. Their upper layers may be contaminated by algae, sometimes even by water-weeds, their lower layers may become polluted by the decomposition of living matter. Costly aqueducts also have to be built to convey the water to the treatment works.

More effective use can be made of both rivers and reservoirs by integrating the two sources—a method known as *river regulation*. For the same cost, river regulation produces a much higher output than using either source separately. When the river flow is adequate, water is

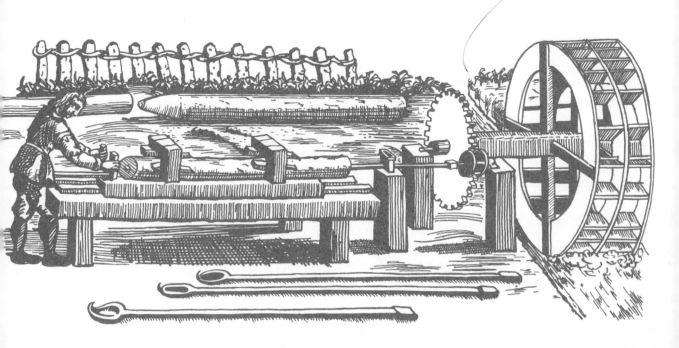

Top: A 17th-century woodcut of "The Pipe Borer." Wooden pipes, mainly of elm, were used for underground mains for about 200 years. Tree-trunks were bored with long augers, driven in this case by a waterwheel. The tapered end of one pipe fitted into the thick end of the next. The joints leaked badly, and could not withstand high pressures. Bottom: An engraving (1749) of one of several London Bridge waterwheels with lifting apparatus. These wheels supplied about 1.8 million gallons daily to London houses.

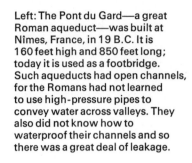

Left: The Pont du Gard—a great Roman aqueduct—was built at Nîmes, France, in 19 B.C. It is 160 feet high and 850 feet long; today it is used as a footbridge. Such aqueducts had open channels, for the Romans had not learned to use high-pressure pipes to convey water across valleys. They also did not know how to waterproof their channels and so there was a great deal of leakage.

The cut-and-cover aqueduct (left) is supported by a bridge to convey water across a valley. If the channel followed the contour of the valley, water would fracture the cover and leak out. The water surface in cut-and-cover aqueducts should therefore not reach the cover. Thus, unlike a pipe, there is a limit to the speed at which water can be pushed through. This is a great problem for some systems. Manchester, England, for example, is allowed to draw water from Ullswater, a lake, but is forbidden to lay pipes through the catchment area. Manchester thus must use the existing cut-and-cover aqueduct, even though it may leak.

taken from the river. Reservoirs are only used as a flood retention basin. When the river level declines, water is added to the river from that accumulated in the reservoir during the previous wet season. River regulation is especially efficient when the river conveys this extra water part or all of the way to the supply area, for it saves the cost of an aqueduct. The benefit, however, is not all one way: The quality of the water inevitably declines with use and re-use in its passage down the river.

Water in rivers, lakes, and reservoirs is called *surface water*. Our last remaining source is *ground water*, which is used in much smaller quantities than surface sources. (In America and Britain it constitutes about 20 per cent of the total supply.) Rarely does a city rely solely on ground water. Occasionally an area obtains its ground water from artesian wells (p. 67). Equally unusual and as fortunate are those areas that obtain water from springs. But in most places, ground water has to be pumped from

wells and boreholes, although with modern pumps this may be quite cheap. The most important considerations are how far away ground water lies from the areas of supply, how deep it lies, its quality, and how much water can be abstracted without permanently lowering the water table (p. 72). A good-quality underground source near a city is an invaluable asset. Often the water is so pure that it needs only to be sterilized before reaching the faucet.

The next stage in water supply is its transmission from the source to the treatment works. Sometimes the water is treated at its source; at other times this is done at the area of supply. The choice depends partly on the risks of pollution en route. Water is taken from rivers, lakes, and reservoirs through an *intake* that is well screened to keep out fish and debris.

The device along which water flows from the source to the treatment works is called an *aqueduct*. As we mentioned before, in some cases it is best to use an existing river for part of

44

Left: Photograph of canal carrying water part of the way from the Sea of Galilee to the Negev desert, Israel. The canal is the oldest type of aqueduct and, despite large losses by evaporation, is still used in certain situations. Ways of preventing seepage have been developed recently, including adding a waterproof lining while the canal is full of water. Below: Photograph of steel mains laid in a tunnel passing under the Thames in England. Pipes in tunnel are easy to inspect and less liable to external corrosion. The tunnel can also carry electricity cables and other services, but is expensive.

the way, but few rivers run the way desired by the water engineer. Canals are the oldest type of aqueduct, and some magnificent examples were built by the Romans. Canals are still used today, but they have several disadvantages, the chief one being that, because they are open, they can only travel downhill. This is why the Romans built giant stone bridges across valleys to support their channels in a gentle and continuous downhill gradient. It is also impossible to increase the flow in canals to any extent, which can be a critical factor in modern water supply. A further disadvantage is evaporation from the water surface in hot, dry weather, which is particularly serious in hot climates. Considerable losses also occur by seepage through the unlined beds of canals in many parts of the world.

Some of these disadvantages are avoided in channels that are both lined and covered, often called "cut-and-cover" channels. These are less liable to pollution and clogging with waterweeds. But since water flows along them under

atmospheric pressure, some polluted water may seep in. As with canals, water cannot flow along cut-and-cover channels under pressure, otherwise leakage would occur.

When high ground obstructs the route, a tunnel is sometimes built through the barrier, With modern methods of tunnel excavation, this is often cheaper than going round the barrier with, say, cut-and-cover channels. Some tunnels act like cut-and-cover channels because the water is under atmospheric pressure. Others act like pipes in that they carry high-pressure water. But both atmospheric and pressure tunnels are difficult to repair if there is a blockage some distance in. The best type of aqueduct is the pipeline. Flow can be increased at will, there is less loss from leakage, and it is not liable to contamination. A pipeline can also carry water across valleys, and is more easily repaired.

After leaving the aqueduct, water from rivers, lakes, and reservoirs often enters a *storage reservoir* (distribution reservoir). Its principal function is to store a reserve of water near the city. From the storage reservoir, water passes to the treatment works, where the system of purification depends mainly on the quality of the incoming water. Treatment often consists of two stages. *Primary treatment* removes the large particles in the water by one of three common methods. The first passes water quickly through rapid sand filters, the second through fine mesh screens, and the third through a chemical blanket. Then, *secondary treatment* completes the clarification of water and further reduces the bacterial content, usually by using sand filter beds. At one or more stages of the treatment, chemicals may be added to correct acidity, hardness, or both. At some stage of treatment the water is sterilized.

Any bacteria that remain are destroyed by chlorine (or ozone) in a *contact tank*, which allows adequate time for the oxidizing agent to act. The tank sometimes also acts as a *balancing tank*, containing an emergency reserve that lasts several hours so that the supply continues when the treatment works is under repair.

Water now passes on to the *distribution system*, consisting of mains, service reservoirs, and booster pumps. A difficult and costly process in any waterworks is the laying and maintenance of mains, since the perfect pipe has yet to be found. In a developed European country a 30-inch-diameter pipe one mile long set 2 feet 6 inches in rock may well cost over $100,000, while the initial cost of a distribution network is about $20 per head in cities and $122 in rural areas. Once the pipes are laid, they also need constant attention. In a city, an average of one fracture a year occurs in every three miles of mains—twice as often as in rural areas. All types of pipes may fracture during the digging of holes for inspecting and laying gas pipes, electricity and telegraph cables, or foundations. Vibration and soil movement caused by traffic, together with natural land subsidence, may add to the damage. Also, in spite of valves and other devices to keep internal water pressures at the right level, occasional surges of high pressure may burst pipes already weakened by other forces. The key factor in the life of a main is corrosion of the inside by "aggressive" water and on the outside by "aggressive" soils. Due to the greater concentration on waste prevention during the last century, leakage from pipelines has fallen by 60 per cent, from 25 to 10 ghd in Britain. This decline has come about despite an almost hundredfold increase in the number of fixtures and longer pipes per head of population, and a threefold increase in pressure. Leakage is normally investigated during the night, with the

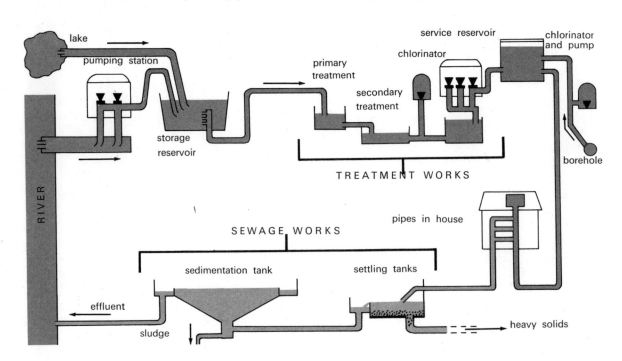

The above diagram follows the passage of water from source (lakes, rivers, boreholes) to storage reservoirs, to treatment plant, and finally to users. Waste water is treated at sewage plant, after which it returns to rivers or lakes.

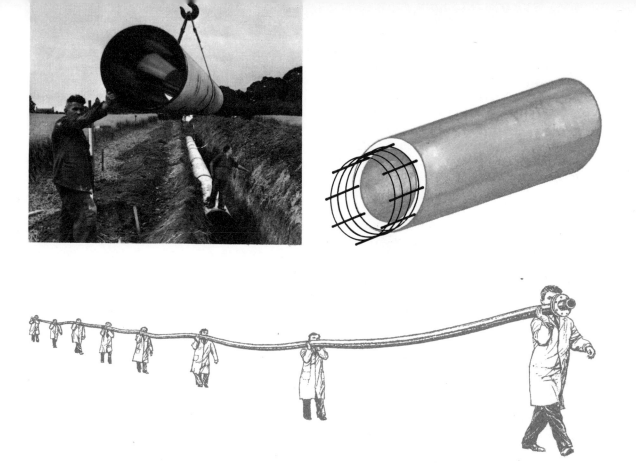

Steel pipes are so strong and flexible that large diameters (top left) need only thin walls. Pipe is coated with bitumen to resist corrosion, and white asbestos protects it from chipping. Reinforced concrete pipes (top right) are thick-walled and heavy. They therefore involve high transport costs, and are used for low-pressure work. Plastic pipes (above) are so light that this 210-foot length can be carried and laid by hand.

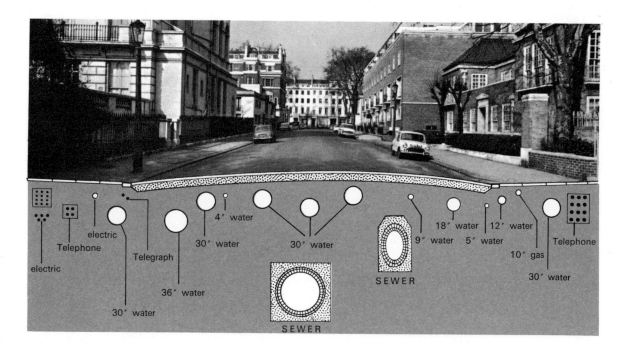

Above: Diagram shows installations below typical city road surface. From the 4-inch mains, a ½-inch service pipe leads to homes. The large mains carry water to other areas. Sewers lie deeper, so that if they fracture, sewage cannot enter leaky mains. There is no standard depth or position for mains in large cities. But today, small mains are usually laid under the pavement, and large mains under the road at a depth of 3 to 7 feet to prevent damage from frost and vibration.

aid of charts that record the consumption of the area. As the streets are closed in turn, a drastic drop appears on the chart when an unknown leak is shut off. Then follows a more intensive and very laborious search for the leak, using sounding sticks or acoustic electronic equipment.

The larger diameter mains (18–60 inches) leading from the treatment works are called *trunk* mains. They divide, like the branches of a tree, into smaller *district* (secondary) mains, which are usually laid under the streets. From these, *service* pipes (up to about 2 inches) lead to buildings. In a country like England, the first mains, dating from the fifteenth century, were made of cast iron. Many laid in the last century still provide good service. The great disadvantage of cast iron is its tendency to corrode. Today this is overcome by lining the pipes with concrete and sheathing them with bitumen. Cast iron has been largely superseded by spun iron and ductile iron pipes.

For large mains up to 60 inches in diameter,

steel is usually the most economical material. Because of its great strength and flexibility, it can be relied on to provide a continuous supply in almost all conditoins. Non-steel pipes, such as those made of cast iron and asbestos cement, collapse completely when they fracture. But steel pipes develop corrosion pit-holes, which can be covered by watertight sleeves, or tubes, while the pipe is still in service. Steel pipes, like those of iron, need protecting from corrosion by bitumen and concrete.

In many cases, prestressed concrete pipes are better than those made of steel, for, as well as being able to withstand high internal pressures, they do not corrode. The pipe is made by molding concrete around steel wires previously placed under tensile stress. When the concrete sets, the steel pulls the concrete together so that water pressures cannot cause cracks in the pipe. For a given water pressure, a prestressed concrete pipe is more economical than one made of steel. But, on the other hand, concrete pipes are very heavy, and if they have to be transported long

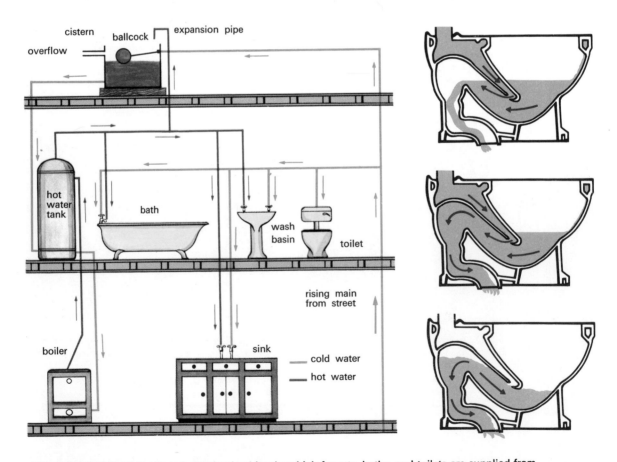

Above: Typical English urban domestic plumbing in which faucets, baths, and toilets are supplied from pipe (at right side). In the hot water system, cold water flows from roof cistern to bottom of hot tank and then to boiler; heated water rises to top of hot tank and then to faucets. If water overheats, expansion pipe relieves pressure into cistern. Above right: Three stages (top to bottom) show how flushing of toilets is designed to regulate the water's flow to avoid waste.

distances, then it is cheaper to use steel pipes.

Another economical type of pipe in sizes up to 30 inches is made from asbestos cement, in which fibers of asbestos reinforce the concrete. Although brittle, this type of pipe is fairly strong, and it only corrodes in sulfate soils. Reinforced concrete pipes are suitable for low-pressure work, such as sewers and some aqueducts. They are used because they are cheaper than prestressed concrete or steel pipes, and can be made in large sizes.

For pipes up to 10 inches in diameter there has recently been a very important development in the field of plastics. Polyethylene pipes are now in common use, being flexible, cheap, and resistant to corrosion. On the other hand, polyethylene is less robust than steel and, in the tropics, termites and baboons have been known to gnaw into these pipes. Also, coal gas is able to pass through its wall from the soil. PVC (polyvinyl-chloride) pipes are more resistant to gas. These are widely used in continental Europe and provide a good alternative to traditional materials where there is no danger of frosty weather.

Service pipes, which lead to houses, are as large as two inches in diameter. Lead is the traditional material for these, and is still used where water is hard. Soft water in lead pipes can cause lead poisoning. Lead pipes first gave way to copper pipes in the 1940s, and then to the cheaper plastic ones. For internal pipes within houses and factories, copper and galvanized iron are now generally used, the former predominating in soft water areas.

In most areas today, water travels from the treatment works, via some of the mains, to *service reservoirs*, feeding some houses on the way. Service reservoirs are roofed over to prevent contamination and keep out light, which would induce the growth of algae. They are situated at such an elevation that gives enough pressure for water to flow to premises under gravity but not enough to produce an excessive flow or burst the mains. When no ground at the right elevation exists, the more costly *water towers* are used. The main purpose of service reservoirs, which fill up at night, is to supplement the flow from the treatment works during day-time peak periods. Service reservoirs also contain from one to two days' supply of water so that the supply can continue when the mains

fail or when they are under repair. When there are considerable variations in height over an area, water may have to be pumped through a succession of service reservoirs at different levels so that each provides enough pressure but not too much.

When water enters a building it automatically rises about four stories under its own pressure. In parts of the United States and in Europe, all domestic plumbing fixtures are under mains pressure, and therefore may leak badly. In South American and Mediterranean cities, when the demand for water is heavy, the mains pressure falls throughout the area so that water fails to reach the upper floors, except in the early hours of the morning. In London and a few other cities, all fixtures, except for one drinking faucet on each floor, are fed by water that flows by gravity from a storage cistern on the roof. The pressue is thus much lower than mains pressure, and fixtures leak less. Moreover, if a main has to be repaired, storage cisterns provide a reserve of at least 60 gallons, which could, in a pinch, last a few days. In tall buildings, booster pumps supplement the mains pressure so that water can reach the upper floors.

For the rest of this chapter we examine the water supply systems of certain areas. We start with New York, a large city with a dense population. New Yorkers are supplied by an upland system of large lakes and reservoirs from which chlorinated water flows by *gravity* to the city. New York also illustrates how even very large water resources can sometimes fail to provide an adequate supply when there is a combination of inadequate planning, a very high leakage rate from the distribution system, and a high consumption.

Apart from a few boreholes on Long Island and Staten Island, New York's water originates in the mountains to the north (diagram p. 52). These sources have a capacity of about 505 billion gallons and also supply several other states, including communities along the Delaware River, of which Philadelphia is the largest. There are three separate reservoir systems feeding New York. The first, built in 1843–1911 in the Croton Mountains 45 miles from the city center, consists of 12 reservoirs and 5 controlled lakes. Two cut-and-cover aqueducts carry water directly to service reservoirs in the city.

Since the Croton Mountains are not very high, they supply water only to the low-lying areas of Manhattan and the Bronx, mostly by gravity.

Between 1905 and 1928, two large reservoirs, linked by a 12-mile tunnel, were constructed in the Catskill Mountains, 125 miles to the north, at a height of 900 feet. These trap the large quantities of spring runoff from rainfall and melting snow for use during the summer. By then, runoff is low due to the high absorption of water by vegetation and the soil and the high rate of evapotranspiration. Leading from the reservoirs is the 92-mile Catskill aqueduct, consisting of cut-and-cover channels, steel-pipe inverted siphons, and pressure tunnels. After passing 1000 feet below the Hudson River, the aqueduct feeds the Kensico storage reservoir 30 miles from New York. This reservoir, with a capacity of 30,000 million gallons (MG), is very useful when the Croton system is interrupted.

The Delaware system, begun in 1936, includes four reservoirs in the Catskill Mountains at a height of about 1400 feet. From these the 130-mile Delaware high-pressure tunnel pours water into the Kensico reservoir. From there it flows on through the Catskill and Delaware aqueducts to the Hillview service reservoir in Yonkers. From here, two city tunnels in hard rock, 18 and 20 miles long, 11 to 21 feet wide, and a few hundred feet below the ground, feed all parts of the city. Water from the tunnels flows under pressure up vertical shafts to the distribution system at the surface.

The large quantities of water supplied to New York are very wholesome, which is one of the advantages of building reservoirs in areas of sparse population. There is little or no need to filter the water, although much is aerated to remove iron and manganese and to improve its taste. Much of the water in both upland and service reservoirs is treated with copper sulfate to check algal growth. All water is chlorinated before passing into supply, sometimes before it enters the aqueduct from the upland reservoirs, and always again as it leaves the aqueduct for the city.

The distribution system contains over 6000 miles of mains up to 72 inches in diameter, mostly of cast iron, steel, and reinforced concrete—a densely packed network in which three-quarters of a mile of mains supply 1000 people.

The network is divided into contoured zones according to street elevations so that consumers in each zone have enough water pressure but not too much. Nearly all water enters the zones under gravity at a pressure of about 50 pounds per square inch, which is sufficient to lift water to the top floor of four-story buildings. About five per cent has to be pumped up to the higher zones. Taller buildings pump water into a roof tank. Skyscrapers pump water successively into tanks on each 10th floor from which water feeds the floors below by gravity.

When a city like New York has such an abundant supply, it is worth examining the causes of the serious water shortage in the summer of 1965. The city's water supply was said to be "drought-proof until the year 2000," and it was stated that "1550 mgd could safely be depended on at all times." The shortage therefore caught both consumers and the municipal authorities somewhat off guard. People were urged to use less water, especially for the unnecessary flushing away in toilets of everything from cigarette ends to paper wrappings. The use of air conditioners was restricted; restaurateurs who supplied customers with a glass of water without request were threatened with a fine; at one stage, no one was allowed to clean his car; Tiffany's, in a humorous gesture, used gin in its fountains instead of water.

The main reason for the water shortage was attributed to a 25 per cent drop in the average rainfall in the northeast of the U.S.A. from 1961 to 1965. In other words, the system was more than a year's supply deficient over the four years. Worse still, the actual runoff was 33 per cent below average, for when it did rain the earth was so dry that it absorbed more than usual. Nevertheless the reservoirs were still 88 per cent full in June 1964. But as the summer and winter of 1964 continued dry, the reservoirs were only 55 per cent full by June 1965, and continued to drop throughout the summer. It was predicted that unless the rainfall reverted to normal in 1966, there would be an even worse shortage the following summer.

The average yearly rainfall in the catchment area for New York is a generous 47 inches. During the four-year drought, this average fell to 34 inches—just below the average for the notoriously wet British Isles. Why then the shortage? The answer is that even 34 inches of rain were not enough for a city with a very high water consumption and leakage rate. New York uses about 1345 mgd (180 ghd) for a population of over 7 million, compared with 440 mgd (70 ghd) supplied to London's 6¼ million.

New York City's high consumption is partly due to the low price of water, which encourages waste in the home, and to the great use of water-consuming mechanical gadgets. An expert committee had already made known that commercial water meters were under-registering by about 48 mgd and suggested that domestic consumers were wasting the same amount. Yet, up to the last moment, New York continued to use unnecessarily large amounts of water, hoping for the return of normal weather conditions. As late as October 1964, the Water Commissioner said: "I do not at present see any danger of a water shortage."

Just as important was the fact that the mains and service reservoirs, many of which were old and inaccessible, leaked badly. The underground waste per person, in fact, equaled the daily consumption per person in Britain of about 60 ghd, which amounted to nearly 480 mgd for the whole city. Another reason for the high leakage was that the pipe network was not designed with a high enough factor of safety against leakage. When a pipeline is newly laid it has to satisfy a specified maximum rate of leakage, and in America this is 24 times higher than in Britain. Of course, it is important to realize the problems involved in waste detection. It is very difficult to locate leaks in a congested and noisy city using acoustic detectors. Yet it only takes 20 holes of one-half inch diameter in the whole pipe network to cause a loss of about a million gallons a day. It is no wonder that an expert committee suggested that at least 240 mgd could be saved by better waste inspection.

To a certain extent the temporary inability of New York's water supply to cope with modern demands was due to the built-in flaws in the municipal government. In New York City there is the Department of Water Supply, Gas and Electricity, created in 1898 on the German pattern, which operates and maintains the *supply* of water within the city. In 1905 the Board of Water was created for developing new *sources* of water. To this day these bodies remain separate

with no common directive, a dangerous procedure where water is concerned. The metering of domestic supplies would have reduced consumption considerably, as has been demonstrated in many parts of the world. However, New York City has never installed meters in individual apartments—where most of its millions live—and to do so today would be an extremely costly decision by the authorities. In New York the Water Commissioner is appointed by the Mayor, who in turn is elected by popular vote. It will be a brave Mayor who will risk losing votes by advocating water metering and increased charges.

But we should not over-criticize the shortcomings of water administrations, which usually learn by hard experience. (Incidentally, by the summer of 1966 the "great drought" crisis collapsed, thanks to increased snow and rain in the crucial areas.) The sensible objective is not a perfect water supply, but a supply *just* adequate to the needs. This means that a city must be prepared to suffer some hardship during really exceptional droughts, and in fact New York did reduce its consumption by 20 per cent during 1965. But a city must be prepared to take steps as best it can and in good time. Many authorities believe that New York should not have relied solely on upland sources, neglecting the large river that runs nearby. Today there is no valid reason why the polluted Hudson should not be used, especially with modern treatment methods. In fact, a treatment works was reconstructed in 1966 at Chelsea on the Hudson (having been dismantled after the drought of 1950) to deliver an extra 120 mgd. By 1966, moreover, a large new Delaware reservoir was also in action to supply 330 mgd.

The water supply of London differs from New York in almost all respects. There are no upland reservoirs, although the idea was suggested a century ago. Instead, the main source is rivers that are heavily polluted, mainly with the sewage effluent of the cities of Oxford and Reading. The water must therefore be carefully filtered and sterilized. All water is *pumped* from the rivers, and then enters a large number of storage reservoirs. To a great extent, the form of London's water system is dictated by its history. When in 1903 the Metropolitan Water Board was formed from eight existing water com-

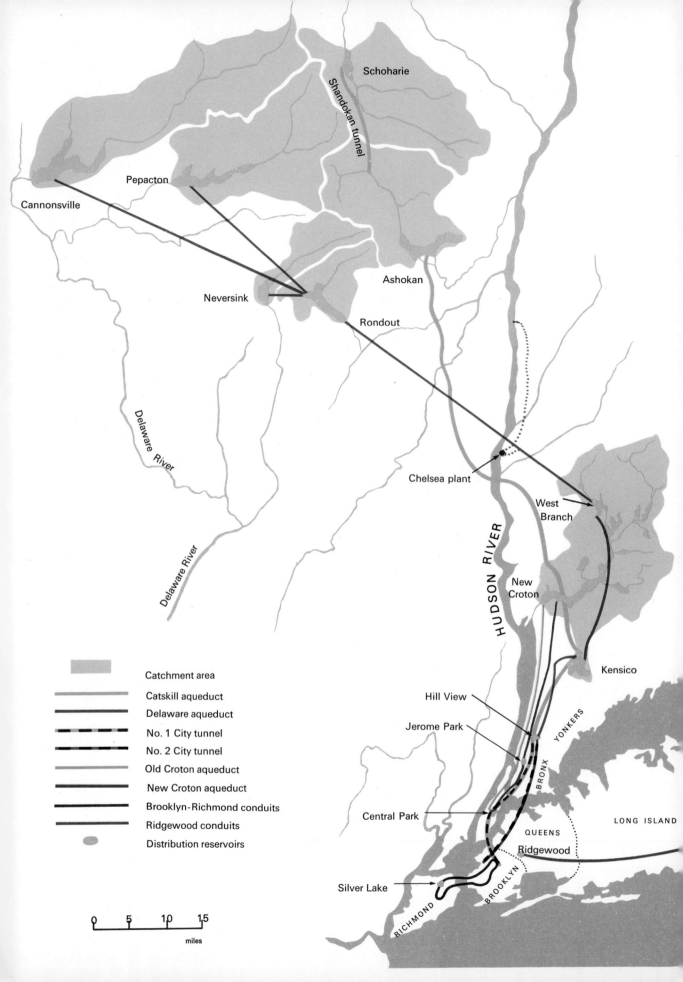

Schoharie

Shandokan tunnel

Pepacton

Cannonsville

Neversink

Ashokan

Rondout

Delaware River

Delaware River

HUDSON RIVER

Chelsea plant

West Branch

New Croton

Kensico

Hill View

Jerome Park

YONKERS

BRONX

Central Park

QUEENS

LONG ISLAND

Ridgewood

Silver Lake

BROOKLYN

RICHMOND

Catchment area

Catskill aqueduct

Delaware aqueduct

No. 1 City tunnel

No. 2 City tunnel

Old Croton aqueduct

New Croton aqueduct

Brooklyn-Richmond conduits

Ridgewood conduits

Distribution reservoirs

0   5   10   15

miles

Right: A balloon hovers over New York City during the summer of 1965, exhorting people to reduce their consumption. At times, no one was allowed to wash cars or to water gardens, and certain restrictions were imposed on the use of air conditioners.

Left: Plan of New York City's water supply system. Below: Flow-chart of same. Until 1966, New York City relied almost entirely on the relatively unpolluted upland lakes and reservoirs to the north. The advantage of using this source is that the water normally needs very little treatment. The disadvantage became apparent during the 1961–65 period of subnormal rainfall, when New Yorkers were compelled to reduce their consumption considerably. Since then a pumping and treatment works has been built on the Hudson River, above the tidal limit at Chelsea, to provide an additional source in the event of further droughts.

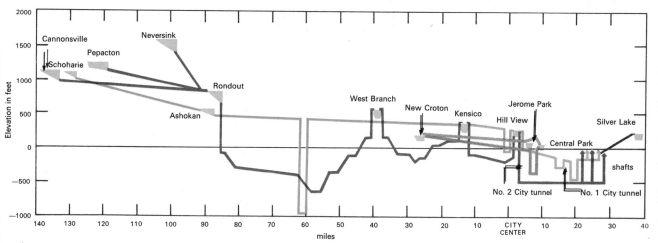

panies, they took over a system that had evolved with little planning since the early seventeenth century. Cautiously, the Board interconnected, adapted, and expanded the complex pipe network, the storage reservoirs, and the old slow sand filter beds. Through the more efficient use of these time-honored methods, and by a scrupulous bacteriological examination of all water, the Board now produces a cheap and reliable supply that continues during both drought and flood.

Sixty-eight per cent of London's water comes from the Thames River, 16 per cent from the Lee River, and 16 per cent from wells and boreholes. The runoff from the catchment area is not high, but fortunately the Thames does not only depend on immediate runoff. Much of the water entering the river comes from springs and ground-water seepage, with a contribution of effluent from sewage works. The Thames is thus a good source because its flow during the dry summer is, to a large extent, maintained by seepage of water that accumulated during the previous winter. However, infiltration is decreasing as new housing estates cover the porous ground with impermeable roads and houses.

London is also fortunate in obtaining good quality water from wells and boreholes, mainly in Kent and in the Lee valley. The city is built over a large chalk basin up to 700 feet thick, covered by a blanket of clay. The exposed porous chalk of the Chiltern Hills and North Downs provides a large *gathering ground* for water to sink downward and flow into the basin under London, where it accumulates. In the past the city derived much of its water from wells, many of which were artesian, but inevitably excessive use of such water has led to gradual depletion. But as we shall see, ground water will play a vital role in the future of London's water supply.

Water is taken from the Thames above its tidal limit at Teddington Weir, where the flow averages 1872 mgd. Normally the Board is not allowed to reduce the flow below 204 mgd. Water passes through several intakes, each well screened to catch debris, before it is pumped into 37 storage reservoirs. The total capacity of these reservoirs, about 30 days' peak supply, is not large compared with the 200 days of many upland reservoirs. They are drawn down only on

the few occasions when the river flow is seriously diminished. An important function of the reservoirs is to reduce the number of bacteria and to allow suspended matter to settle out. The reservoirs provide the usual algal outbursts, which may impede the flow through sand filters and give water a taste. But this has been alleviated by forced circulation in the reservoir and by dosing with chemicals.

From the storage reservoirs, water passes to the treatment works, where primary filtration involves passing water quickly through rapid sand filter beds or microscreens. These hold back coarse suspended matter, including algae, and prevent it from reaching and blocking the more critical secondary treatment in the slow sand-beds. As water passes very slowly through slow sandbeds, a very large filtration area of 154 acres is needed. No chemical methods of filtration are used in London. Nor are chemicals added during filtration to correct acidity or hardness. This is in marked contrast to modern practice in most other large waterworks.

All water finally receives a small dose of chlorine, after which it passes into a large contact tank. Here water stays for a long time, and only a trace of chlorine remains when it enters the distribution system. Water from wells rarely needs filtering, but as a safety measure receives a heavy dose of chlorine followed by dechlorination with sulfur dioxide. This entire process is known as *superchlorination*.

A distribution network of some 9000 miles of underground mains, interconnected with 92 service reservoirs and water towers, supplies an area of 540 square miles. Water from the treatment works has to be pumped into the mains, the old ones of cast iron, the new ones of bitumen-lined steel pipes. For ready access beneath rivers, tunnels are used to carry pipes, and a 19-mile pressure tunnel has been driven to transfer Thames water to the Lee valley, using the natural surrounding clay as the impervious wrapper. After repeated branching, the trunk mains end up by supplying buildings and homes through a lead service pipe.

No more water can be taken either from the Lee River or from the present boreholes. The Thames could supply more water than it does already if more storage reservoirs were built, but they are expensive to build and no more land is available. The Metropolitan Water Board therefore takes great care to conserve its water and to eliminate waste. Another reason for water conservation is that every drop has to be expensively pumped through several stages—from the river into the storage reservoirs, to the treatment works, to the mains, to the service reservoirs. Booster pumps lift water to high ground and to tall buildings. In other words, over 400 mgs have to be pumped at least three times for the consumers.

The English place emphasis on the detection of leaks in the mains and service reservoirs. The Board also depends heavily on the good nature of its consumers to report leakage and not to waste water. Since two-thirds of the supply is domestic and unmetered, there is no way in which the board can detect if a consumer wastes water. But Londoners consume only about 70 ghd, which is very little compared with many other cities of Europe.

As for the future of London's water supply, there is little land left for more storage reservoirs. It is therefore proposed to drill numerous boreholes into the large chalk aquifers under the western end of the Thames valley, covering 900 square miles of the counties of Berkshire, Wiltshire, and Gloucestershire. These will supply an extra 324 mgd, which will be pumped into the tributaries of the Thames when the river is at its summer low. In winter the ground water will be allowed to replenish itself. The Thames will thus be used as a natural pipeline, and although this means that clean ground water is added to polluted river water, it will be cheaper than building a long pipeline. It will also help to dilute sewage effluents in the river.

Having described the supply of two cities, we now turn to a rural area—Mid Cheshire, England (diagram p. 60). Here a relatively small quantity of water (15.6 mgd) is supplied to a large area of 500 square miles. Cheshire's special feature is the integration of underground and surface supplies by a simple process to make the best use of both. Ground water is deliberately underdrawn in wet weather when the river level is high, and overdrawn in dry weather when the river is low. This prevents the water table from permanent decline and increases the availability of water in drought. In addition to this integration of sources for local use, the river and upland reservoirs are combined for river regulation over a wider area.

Mid Cheshire was also the first European authority to install a computer to type out incoming data from widely distant pumping stations. This type of computer eliminated the necessity of reading dials and resulted in a very efficient water-supply system. The running of all waterworks is affected by human fallibility. It was found, for example, that 60 per cent of night plant failures were caused by mistakes made during the day. It was also discovered that man is less efficient and more expensive than an automatic alarm. This type of automation freed skilled staff from the laborious task of continually watching dials and keeping charts of information, just in case something went wrong.

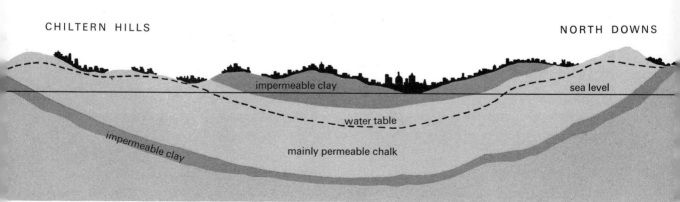

CHILTERN HILLS

NORTH DOWNS

impermeable clay

sea level

impermeable clay

water table

mainly permeable chalk

Above: A diagrammatic section through the London Basin in which the vertical scale is exaggerated. The aquifer, which is mainly chalk, is up to 700 feet thick, and lies between two layers of impermeable clay. Rain seeps into the exposed aquifer on the Chiltern Hills and North Downs, and flows down toward London. Ground water was once a major source of supply, but it has been seriously overdrawn. Today ground water supplies only 16 per cent of London's water.

HERTFORD

EPPING

Boundary of direct water supply
Sludge disposal works
Storage reservoir
Filtration works
Sewage treatment works

0   5   10
                    miles

EDGWARE

Rammey Marsh
King George's
William Girling
Deephams

Lockwood
Warwick
Lee Bridge

ILFORD

Stoke Newington

LONDON

Beckton

Crossness

Perry Oaks

EALING

Barn Elms

Mogden
Kew

King George VI

Queen Mary
Ashford

Teddington Weir
Wandle Valley

RIVER THAMES

GRAVESEND

Knights
Walton
Island Barn
Hogsmill

ESHER

CROYDON

WESTERHAM

SEVENOAKS

river   pumping station   storage reservoir   primary filter

clay

12:300   450

The map on the left shows the 540 square miles to which the Metropolitan Water Board of London supplies over 400 mgd. Of special interest is the large number of storage reservoirs, which store river water as a reserve for dry periods, and in which polluted water naturally purifies itself to a large extent. About 68 per cent of London's supply comes from the Thames River above Teddington Weir, a further 16 per cent from the Lee River, and the remaining 16 per cent from boreholes. The map also shows the sewage treatment and sludge disposal works. London's sewage effluent empties only into the tidal part of the Thames, which is not used for water supplies.

Above: The first public drinking fountain in London used filtered water from the New River Company. The fountain was mainly for the benefit of the poor, and was an attempt to provide people with an acceptable alternative to alcohol.

The flow-chart below follows the stages that London's water passes through on its way to users. The figures denote the progressive decrease in numbers of bacteria in a half-pint glass of water. Note that this large system uses slow sand filter beds with no chemical treatment except chlorination.

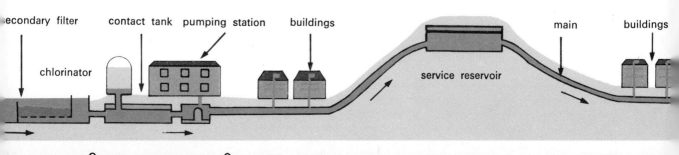

secondary filter   contact tank   pumping station   buildings   main   buildings

chlorinator   service reservoir

The computer digested the incoming data, discarding the unimportant, and gave the alarm only when something went wrong. Thus not only were errors reduced, but the staff had time for more skilled work, heavy labor costs were saved, and productivity was doubled.

In Britain's first river regulation project, Mid Cheshire, Wrexham, East Denbighshire, Wirral, and Liverpool formed a consortium with the river authority to control the flow of the Dee River in central Wales by two regulating reservoirs. Lake Bala is a natural lake (capacity, 4080 MG) in which sluice gates have been inserted in the natural barrier across its outlet. During the dry summer, the declining river flow is augmented by water from the reservoir. In anticipation of winter floods, the reservoir is kept low in order to accommodate floodwaters that would otherwise damage agricultural property in the valley below. The other regulating reservoir, called Llyn Tryweryn (capacity, 20,400 MG), is formed by an earth dam, and supplements water from Bala Lake.

For Mid Cheshire in particular, water is pumped from the Dee River into the 40-mile-long Llangollen canal, constructed in 1795-1805. The water gravitates leisurely to an old raw-water reservoir at the Hurleston treatment works, crossing difficult ground by attractive stone bridges, one of which is reminiscent of the aqueducts of ancient Rome. Canals, as we have pointed out, are not the ideal type of aqueduct, especially unlined ones, since they experience large losses by seepage and evaporation. In order to get 9.6 mgd to Hurleston during very dry weather, nearly twice as much has to be pumped from the Dee. The reasons for using the canal in Mid Cheshire are the same as those in favor of rivers rather than pipelines—the canal was already there, it ran in the right direction, and the cost of a more efficient pipeline would have been much greater.

From the Hurleston reservoir (capacity, 108 MG), water passes to the treatment works, which uses efficient chemical methods. Primary filtration consists of the upward flow of water through a blanket, mainly of aluminum hydroxide, which removes the large particles. At the same time, chlorine is added to kill bacteria and control algal growths. The water is drawn off from the top and passed to rapid-gravity sand filters. After this, lime is added to correct acidity, and water travels to the contact tank (capacity, 2.4 MG) where it remains for six hours before entering the distribution system.

In this waterworks, great pains are taken to ensure complete sterilization by using large amounts of chlorine and then dechlorinating with sulfur dioxide. This is partly necessary because the bacterial count of the Dee River is higher than it is for London's water after it has been stored. The process is a little more expensive than the marginal chlorination used in London and New York, but it does ensure that absolutely wholesome water always enters the distribution network.

From the contact tank, 9.6 mgd is pumped into the 1400-mile network of mains. These are connected at the perimeter with those of neighboring authorities to give help in times of drought. Some consumers receive water as it passes *to* service reservoirs. The majority receive water *from* the service reservoirs. For those living on high ground, such as Mow Cop (1090 feet), water passes through as many as seven reservoirs by consecutive pumping.

Mid Cheshire is fortunate in having a great expanse of thick underground sandstone, which supplies 7.2 mgd of excellent quality water—almost as much as is taken from the Dee River. The Delamere boreholes, 36 inches in diameter, penetrate 800 feet into the sandstone, although the water level is only 100 feet below ground level. They thus expose a large vertical area of water-bearing rock. The cost of pumping 1200 gallons 100 feet to ground level and then a further 150 feet to the service reservoirs is only about four cents, compared with about 21 cents for river water treatment. The natural quality of the water is so high that only marginal chlorination is needed before pumping into the supply system.

We end this chapter by describing the supply system of two cities in Germany, both of which use very interesting techniques. Much of Germany overlies a generous supply of cool, clear ground water, supplying as much as 75 per cent of the nation's needs. Most of it comes from shallow wells and boreholes. The ground water is usually not too hard, but it often contains objectionable amounts of carbon dioxide, iron, and manganese. In such cases the water is

Great Britain's Llangollen canal (in 19th-century etching above) was built for navigation. Now it also carries water from the Dee River, Wales, to the water treatment plant in Cheshire, England.

filtered (usually by rapid and slow sand filters); chemical treatment is rarely used. Carbon dioxide is removed with lime, the iron by aeration followed by sand filtration, and the manganese by filtration through zeolites (p. 139) on which the manganese is deposited.

The water supply of Essen (population 835,000) is typical of several towns in the Ruhr and Rhine valleys, where very polluted river water is filtered through the alluvial sides of the river. This process starts when raw river water is diverted over a small dam into a large sedimentation basin. After some 12 hours' retention there, the water passes on to about 52 acres of filter beds. These are excavated out of the banks of the river by removing the natural silt until the gravel is exposed, which is then covered with sand. After a time, the top layer of sand becomes clogged and is then skimmed and replaced. Water seeps through the beds until it reaches perforated collector pipes 30 feet down and gravitates to wells on the other side of the river. No artificial filtration is necessary, and after adding chlorine, water passes into the supply. This process, which makes full use of nature, amounts in fact to a conversion of polluted river water into clean ground water. Essen's average consumption of 39.6 mgd is met by this system at the high cost of 52 cents per 1000 gallons.

Munich is a large city with a population of over one million, which obtains all its water from underground. There are 7000 private wells in and around the city, mainly for industrial use. Drinking water comes from more distant wells and from an interesting system of *infiltration galleries* built in 1883. These are horizontal tunnels, or adits, about three to five feet in diameter, built in pervious rock and slotted to allow ground water to seep into them. They are situated 300 feet above the city, in the Mangfall valley of the Bavarian Alps, about 25 miles from Munich. Water flows from many of these galleries by gravity along aqueducts to two large, covered reservoirs near the city (capacity, 45.6 MG). The rest is pumped from wells in the valley into the aqueducts. One reservoir supplies the higher zones of the city, the other the low zones. Their relative height is such that water flows by gravity to each zone at the right pressure. The high-quality water obtained needs only chlorination. The cost per 1000 gallons is 27 cents. Again, this is a rather high figure if we consider that the generous natural supply does not need extensive treatment and also requires very little pumping.

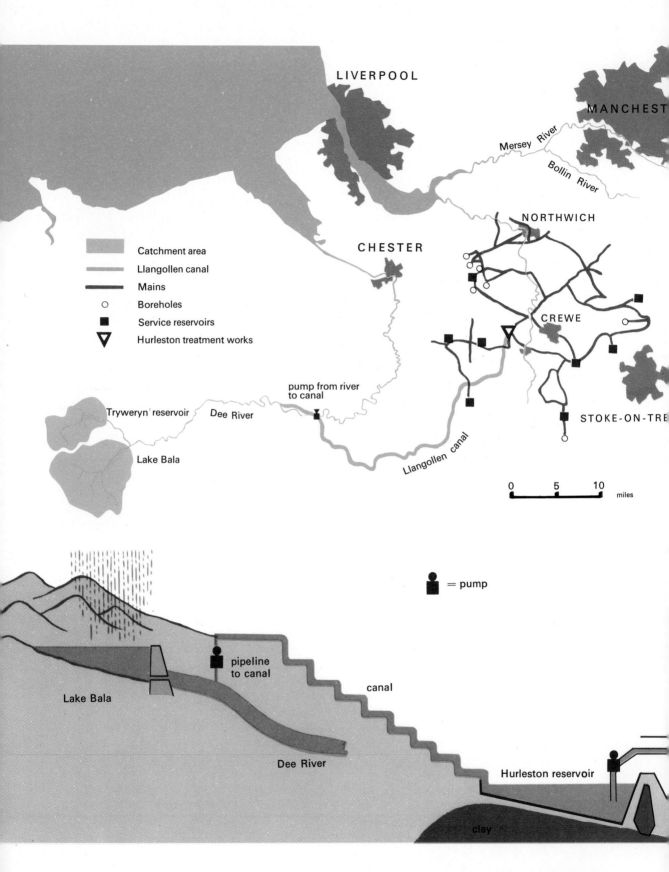

LIVERPOOL

MANCHEST

Mersey River

Bollin River

NORTHWICH

CHESTER

CREWE

STOKE-ON-TRE

Catchment area

Llangollen canal

Mains

○ Boreholes

■ Service reservoirs

▽ Hurleston treatment works

pump from river
to canal

Tryweryn reservoir   Dee River

Lake Bala

Llangollen canal

0   5   10

miles

■ = pump

Lake Bala

pipeline
to canal

canal

Dee River

Hurleston reservoir

clay

Top: Map of supply area of England's Mid Cheshire
Water Board. Water from the Dee River passes to
Hurleston treatment works by canal. The river flow is
controlled by two regulating reservoirs. Bottom: Flow-
chart shows principal stages from source to faucet.

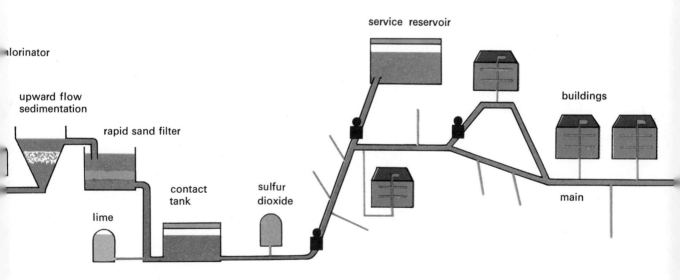

Top: The pump room at Hurleston, England, where the flow to the rapid sand filter beds is regulated. Chemicals are fed into the water from yellow tanks as part of the treatment. These chemicals, however, do not affect the water's safety and palatability.

61

Left: Photograph of an infiltration gallery—a horizontal tunnel in permeable rock into which water trickles. The concrete-lined drainage channel connects with others and they all converge on a basin from which water is pumped to the surface. Munich, Germany (below), is a city that obtains its supply in this way.

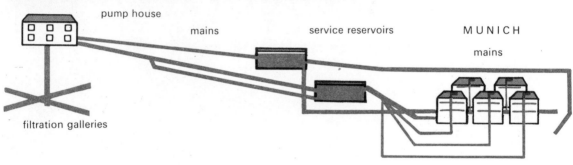

pump house

mains

service reservoirs

MUNICH

mains

filtration galleries

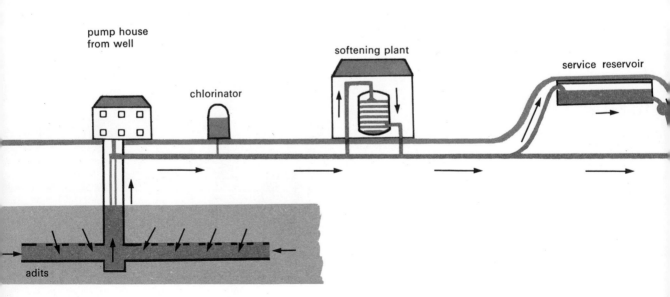

pump house
from well

chlorinator

softening plant

service reservoir

adits

There are about 3500 private wells like this one (right) being built in Calcutta, India. The city is short of about 60 mgd, so every possible source has to be exploited. Much of the water is so unsanitary that there are frequent epidemics of cholera and typhoid.

The Cambridge Water Company in England supplies about 450 square miles. All its water comes from underground, mostly from a chalk aquifer that overlies impermeable clay. Brick-lined tunnels, or *adits*, into which water seeps, radiate out from the base of each well. There is no need for filtration, but Cambridge differs from many English hard-water systems in softening all its water.

CAMBRIDGE

villages

6 Ground Water

It is often said, as if to encourage the hope of increasing our future water resources, that there is more water within the top half-mile of the earth's crust than in all the rivers and lakes combined. True as this may be, what really matters is the proportion of ground water that can be made economically available. At present we do not know how much this is, but we do know that it is only a small fraction of the total. Some ground water lies so deep that it is uneconomic to raise it to the surface. Much of the water is too far away from the supply area. And often it is too heavily mineralized, or dangerously polluted by surface water.

Because ground water is normally invisible (that is, unseen from the earth's surface) the study of its distribution and movements has been much neglected and misunderstood in the past. This has often led to overpumping, which has depleted the amount stored. Today the dangers of exhausting this extremely valuable source are better realized. Obviously, no more water should be taken out of the ground than goes in. When replenishment is slow, less can be withdrawn than when it is fast. But there is more to the effective use of ground water than this. To withdraw ground water safely, we need to know how much of the rainfall seeps through the soil, how fast ground water moves, how one area of ground water feeds another, and so on. In recent years a complex science has developed (including detailed geological surveys, test-boreholes over a wide area, and the use of radio waves) in order to relate these variables.

Aristotle (fourth century B.C.) believed that all ground water derived from the condensation of atmospheric water vapor underground. We now know that only small amounts of ground water form in this way, mainly where there are heavy mountain fogs, desert sand dunes, or limestone caves. A small quantity of ground water also exists where surface water has been trapped during the formation of sedimentary rocks, as under the Californian valley. This *connate* water is usually very saline and therefore useless. Just as useless is *juvenile* water, formed deep in the earth's crust by chemical and physical action. It was the Roman engineer Vitruvius (first century B.C.) who first proposed that ground water was derived from the infiltration of rain. But it was not until the seventeenth century A.D. that this was confirmed by experiment.

Strictly speaking, the term *ground water* includes all water below the earth's surface. In practice, the term is only used for that which can be withdrawn by man. We begin by discussing how rain (or melted snow and hail) reaches the ground water zone. When rain falls on the surface of reasonably dry and permeable ground, some of it enters small channels, or interstices, and travels through them into the *soil zone*. There are many such interstices in fertile soil, formed by the successive moistening and drying of the soil, by the boring of worms, by tunnels left by decayed plant roots, and by the expansion of water on freezing. In the soil zone, water clings to soil particles by surface tension, while some soil particles absorb water like a sponge. After a light rainfall, all the water may

A belief prevailed in the Middle Ages that a spring existed in the Garden of Eden (above) from which flowed the Indus, Tigris, Euphrates, and Nile rivers.

Ground water shows itself naturally when it emerges as a spring. In the spring above, water seeped downward until it reached impermeable rock. It then ran through an overlying fissure until it found an escape. Other springs appear where an aquifer is directly exposed on a hillside.

be retained in the soil zone, so that none is left to travel farther downward. The proportion held also depends on the dryness of the soil. A short, heavy downpour after a dry spell may all be retained. It is even possible that during a period of fairly high total rainfall, all the water is held in the soil zone. This could happen if frequent showers have been interspersed with intense dry periods. The maximum amount of water that can be absorbed by the soil zone—called the *field capacity*—is important agriculturally. It indicates the maximum amount of water available for plant growth.

When the field capacity is exceeded, the surplus water drains down into the *transition zone*, or *zone of aeration*. Any water not held in this zone continues to travel downward until it meets an impermeable layer, above which it accumulates to form the *ground water zone*. The layer through which ground water moves is called the *aquifer*, and its upper surface is known as the *water table*. In practice the water table may not be a well-defined surface, because water sometimes travels up from the aquifer for a few feet by capillarity to form a *capillary fringe*. This water may be absorbed by plant roots, but since it cannot be withdrawn by man, it is not considered part of the aquifer.

To be of any value, an aquifer must have two properties: It should hold a plentiful supply of water, and the water should flow reasonably quickly. The amount of water stored depends on the *porosity*, which is a measure of the size and number of spaces in the rock. Not all water contained in these interstices can be withdrawn, because some water is held in this zone in the same way as in the soil zone. The rate at which ground water flows is determined by the aquifer's *permeability*, and varies from a few feet per day to a few feet per year. Permeability depends on both the size of the pores and the extent to which they are interconnected. Without ground water flow, wells and boreholes would never be replenished, and ground water could not be exploited. In those cases where ground water drains away very slowly, the water table may rise as high as the land surface, so that the topsoil becomes waterlogged.

To withdraw its water economically, an aquifer should have both high permeability and porosity. Clay, for example, makes a bad aquifer

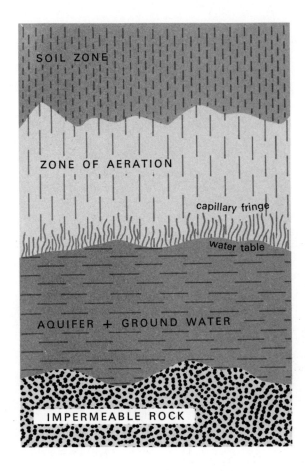

Above: Diagram of distribution of water in ground. In the *soil zone*, water either forms a film around particles, or is adsorbed. Any surplus water gravitates to the *zone of aeration*, where it is held as in the soil zone. From here, any surplus moves down until it meets impermeable rock, and saturates the overlying rock, or *aquifer*, to form *ground water*. From the upper surface of the ground water— the *water table*—water can move up a few feet by capillarity into the zone of aeration.

Right: Diagram of different types of aquifer. In an *unconfined aquifer*, water table is under atmospheric pressure and rises and falls according to amount of recharge (at C—D), outflow, and usage. The water table often undulates and its level roughly corresponds to that in a resting well. A *confined aquifer* lies between two impermeable strata. The water level in a well is at about the same level as the water in the recharge area (A—B) and is therefore higher than the top of the aquifer near the well. The *piezometric surface* corresponds to the pressure of water in the whole aquifer, and if it lies above ground, a gushing artesian well can be built. A *perched aquifer* occurs when water is trapped by a small stratum of impermeable rock.

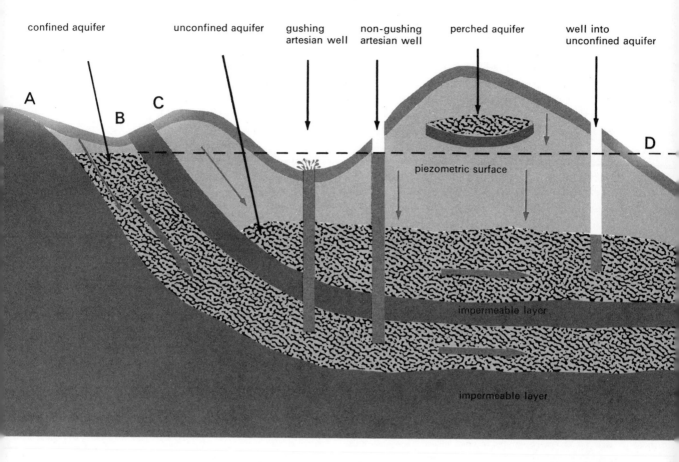

confined aquifer   unconfined aquifer   gushing artesian well   non-gushing artesian well   perched aquifer   well into unconfined aquifer

A

B

C

piezometric surface

impermeable layer

impermeable layer

D

because it has a very high porosity but negligible permeability. Aquifers with high porosities and permeabilities are sands, gravels, some sandstones, and alluvial deposits. The opposite is true of some volcanic rocks, such as granite. Formations such as basalt and some limestones are good aquifers not because they are porous or permeable but because they are full of cracks. In such rocks, water flows very quickly—so quickly that there is little time for contaminants to be filtered out. Thus such aquifers may be polluted, Because each aquifer has a unique size, shape, porosity, permeability, stratification, inclination, and supply of rain, each must be evaluated individually to determine its potential. In the dense, unfissured limestone of the island of Malta, a borehole yields about 0.12 mgd, while a borehole in many red sandstones yields as much as 7.2 mgd.

Ground water strata, or layers, fall into two distinct categories (see illustration above). In an *unconfined aquifer*, water percolates or, seeps,

down until it meets an impermeable layer, above which it accumulates. The water table is under atmospheric pressure, which means that it rises and falls according to the amount of inflow and outflow. The water levels in a group of wells sunk into the aquifer indicate the level of the water table.

A *confined*, or *artesian*, *aquifer* is sandwiched between two impermeable strata, and generally lies beneath an unconfined aquifer. Here the ground water pressure is greater than atmospheric, because water enters the aquifer at a height. The water pressure in a well is roughly equal to the difference in elevation between the well and the point where water enters the aquifer. It also depends to a small extent on the weight of the overlying impermeable layer. In confined aquifers, water rises under pressure up a well to a level higher than the aquifer itself. The level that water would reach under pressure for every point in the aquifer is called the *piezometric surface*. It is calculated by sinking boreholes with sealed tops and recording the water pressures and thus the water levels in the boreholes.

In the past, when small quantities of water were laboriously lifted from ordinary wells by man or beast, artesian wells were discoveries of great value, yielding large quantities for little effort. When the piezometric surface occurred above ground, water actually gushed from these boreholes, produced without any effort other than that of making the hole. Artesian wells are not so important today, because many have been overdrawn, but some are still indispensable in arid areas. Of the six large artesian basins of Australia, the Great Basin in the east covers 678,000 square miles and supplies 492 mgd—the only source of water during the long dry season. Most of the water is used for livestock because it is usually too saline for crops.

The area where water enters the ground to replenish an aquifer is called the *recharge area*. The rate of recharge depends on the area, the average precipitation, and the proportion of precipitation that enters the soil and travels past the soil zone. Up to now, man has been unable to do much to increase the *natural* recharge of aquifers. Experiments to increase rainfall, for example, have had little success. But man can do much to decrease recharge, especially by overgrazing and deforestation. In many developed countries, former recharge areas are now covered with houses and impermeable roads, from which precipitation discharges into drains and sewers instead of recharging the aquifer. This may become a serious problem in some areas.

There is also a movement of water from aquifers into rivers, lakes, and seas. Water that escapes into the sea is, of course, lost to man. Water entering rivers and lakes serves a useful purpose by raising their levels. Ground water replenishment of rivers, such as the Thames, maintains the high flow needed during a dry summer. In some rivers, ground water regulates the flow in the following way. During the flood period, water leaves the permeable riverbed to augment the ground water; when the river level falls, ground water returns through the riverbed.

If the lower end of an aquifer is exposed on a sloping land surface the result is a *spring*. This is distinguished from a seepage area, such as a marsh, by the fact that water flows as a definite current. Most springs yield either small quantities or large amounts for only part of the year. They seldom produce enough to meet the needs of a large community. One large spring that yields large quantities of water (660 mgd) all through the year is the Thousand Springs of the Snake River plain in Idaho. Such springs usually emerge from certain basalts or sandstones, although a few, such as the Silver Springs in Florida (900 mgd), are formed in limestone. The most profuse of all is the spring at Vaucluse, France, whose estimated yield of 2400 mgd would be enough to supply all the domestic consumers in Britain.

Throughout history, man has increased the escape of ground water by sinking wells. Today there are hundreds of thousands of wells and boreholes all over the world, as well as many infiltration galleries. Hand-excavated wells are

Top right: A typical Australian scene of aridity, bones, and a solitary well. This farmer lost 1800 cattle through drought. Wells and boreholes, many of them artesian, are the only source of water in much of Australia.

In an *influent stream* (center), water seeps through the bed to produce a hump in the water table. A stream flowing over an alluvial plain of sand or gravel can quickly disappear by seepage, but the water can be retrieved by sinking wells into the banks or the dry bed. An *effluent stream* (bottom) is one that receives water from an aquifer. The proportion of river-flow due to such seepage is called the *base flow*, and does not fluctuate like water derived from runoff. The base flow, in fact, is often the only river water left during a drought. A stream may be influent at one place, effluent at another; or an influent stream may become effluent as the river-flow and level of water table change.

The spring at Vaucluse, France (far right), results from water gushing out of rock over a wide area. Sometimes it yields about 2.4 billion gallons daily— enough to supply all the domestic consumers of Britain. But like most springs, its flow fluctuates violently from season to season and from year to year.

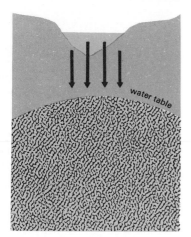

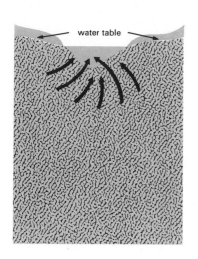

Right: Diagram of typical borehole with submerged electric pump (B) from which a rising main leads water to the surface. Some boreholes have motor at surface from which a spindle passes through rising main to drive pump. Upper part of borehole is lined with pipe and cement to exclude polluted surface water. Lower part of borehole has a slotted lining (A) through which water seeps from aquifer. Fine solids passing through slotted lining fall to bottom of hole, well clear of pumps. Sometimes gravel is packed between slotted lining and rock to keep back solids. Note that water table (C), and hence the standing water level in borehole, is horizontal only when pump is not in use. During pumping, a *cone of depression* forms so that actual level in borehole is well below water table.

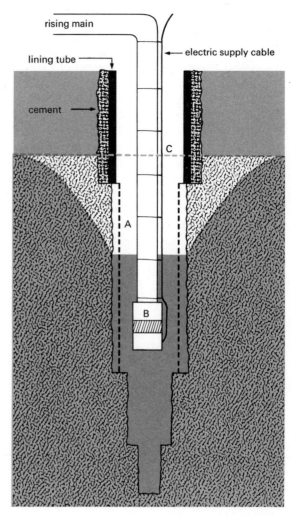

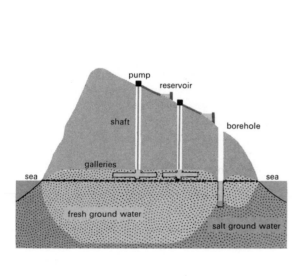

Some 37 miles of infiltration galleries (above) now supply the island of Malta with about 10 mgd. The water table lies only 10 feet above sea level. In such cases, galleries are better than boreholes because they are less liable to be contaminated by sea water when overdrawn. Even so, excessive use has resulted in some contamination, and there are plans for a desalination plant as a supplementary source.

Opposite: Photographs of ancient methods of lifting ground water that are still used. Top left: A great Roman well, 150 feet in diameter and 200 feet deep. Top right: A line of wells in the Algerian Sahara, symbolizing the desert's most precious resource. Bottom left: A man lifts water by means of a *shadoof*, which consists simply of a bucket with a pole and counterpoise. Bottom right: An Archimedean screw—still one of the commonest Egyptian methods of lifting water small distances.

usually a few feet in diameter and up to 50 feet deep. Some of the largest—up to 60 feet in diameter and 250 feet deep—were built by the Romans in Arabia, and by the Russians in Bulgaria. Boreholes, 4 to 60 inches in diameter, may be drilled to a depth of more than 1000 feet. Although the design of wells and boreholes varies, they all penetrate some distance into the aquifer so as to tap as much of the water-bearing face as possible. At the region where water seeps into the well, screens prevent particles from entering the well and pump. The upper part of the well is carefully sealed to prevent the entry of polluted surface water.

One way of withdrawing ground water is by deliberately overpumping, which amounts to mining water like iron ore or petroleum. There is nothing wrong with this method if there are new sources available when the wells dry up. The mining of ground water is inevitable when the rate of replenishment is extremely slow—as in parts of the Sahara, where water has taken about 30,000 years to travel from the recharge area. Even so, overpumping poses problems before the aquifer is finally exhausted. Pumping costs increase as water is overdrawn and the water level is depressed, and water at increasing depths may be heavily mineralized. Land subsidence may also occur, as in Alameda Square in the center of Mexico City, which is sinking at the rate of nearly one foot a year because of continuous pumping from the underlying waterlogged volcanic ash.

Ideally, the water table or piezometric surface should not be allowed to fall permanently. Since there is a time lag between water entering the recharge area and reaching the well, minor temporary falls do not matter. This is just as well in areas whose rainfall varies widely from year to year. Here the aquifer acts as a concealed storage reservoir from which water can be overdrawn in dry years and then left to recharge during a wet year.

Although confined and unconfined aquifers recharge in much the same way, they behave differently when water is being taken out. In unconfined aquifers, withdrawal reduces the amount stored so that the water table drops. In confined aquifers a reduction in pressure accompanies a reduction in the amount stored. The overlying impermeable layer is partly supported by the pressure of the contained water, and as the pressure falls, the aquifer is compressed. If the aquifer is elastic, as it often is, the pressure builds up again as soon as pumping stops. In other cases, the aquifer may be permanently deformed. This has happened in certain parts of the world, resulting in subsidence of the land, and buildings that lean at crazy angles.

Ground water is usually almost entirely free from bacteria, which gives it a valuable advantage as a source for public water supplies. It is also of even temperature, which is very useful for certain industries. Generally, however, ground water contains more salts than does surface water, since it has more contact with, and therefore more time to dissolve, part of the soil and rocks. Mineralization starts as soon as water seeps through the soil zone, because absorption and transpiration of water by plants concentrate the salts in the soil water. In arid areas, rapid evaporation from the soil seriously increases the salt concentration. If there is, in addition, a slow rate of flow in the aquifer, the ground water may quickly become too mineralized and saline to be used.

Although ground water is often quite heavily mineralized, large quantities of it are used in several countries. Ground water is the only source in Malta; in Germany it constitutes over 70 per cent of the total; in Israel about 54 per cent; and in America and Britain about 20 per cent. Sometimes the water needs only chlorination before use. But even when it contains such objectionable minerals as iron and manganese, to remove them—as is common practice in Germany—may still be worthwhile. But the com-

Rain that is unable to sink past the soil zone produces waterlogging and sometimes swelling and slipping of the soil. Left: This apartment block in San Francisco collapsed after heavy rains had saturated and shifted the soil on the hillside.

The stalactites and stalagmites (above) result from the evaporation of ground water so that the dissolved salts are precipitated. The red streaks are due to iron salts. Ground water often contains high salt concentrations, some of which may be harmful. Below: Some waterworks employ a water-taster; chemical tests may prove a source wholesome, but in practice it can taste revolting.

pound that cannot be easily removed is ordinary salt (sodium chloride). Of great importance, therefore, is the contamination of aquifers by *sea-water intrusion*. In an aquifer that discharges on the shoreline, there is a fairly distinct line of contact a short way inland between fresh and salt water (see illustration below). The fresh water floats on top of the denser sea water, with very little mixing between the two. As long as the water table is above sea level and slopes toward the sea, water flows seaward and aquifers along coastlines and on islands yield fresh water. But with rapidly increasing demands for fresh water in many populous coastal areas and islands, the naturally seaward-sloping gradient of the water table has been reduced, or even reversed, drawing the salt/fresh-water line inland.

One of the earliest examples of sea-water intrusion in England occurred in 1855, when saline water entered wells in London and Liverpool from the tidal reaches of their rivers. Since then, overpumping has led to serious contamination of coastal aquifers in Germany, the Netherlands, Japan, and many parts of America. In 1964 the extensive California coastline contained about 13 contaminated aquifers in an area of 150 square miles. It is the price paid for using ground water to supply a large population regardless of hydrological conditions.

The various methods used to overcome salt-water intrusion are all as expensive as they are necessary. The simplest solution is to postpone withdrawing water until the water table rises again above sea level. But this is very inconvenient and costly, because water has to be brought in from other sources. For this reason, Malta is commissioning a 1.2 mgd desalination plant to allow its contaminated aquifers time to regain their natural fresh-water balance. Another method is to flush out the salt and raise the water table by artificially recharging the contaminated aquifer with surface water, although this again requires clean water from other sources. However, Californians are considering the use of flood water and purified waste water that would otherwise discharge into the sea. They are also trying to repel sea water by creating an artificial fresh-water ridge adjacent and parallel to the coast, fed by a line of recharge wells.

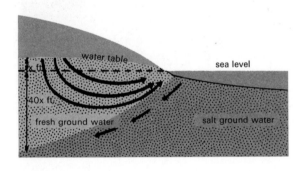

Left: Vertical section through a coastal zone. The lighter fresh water floats on the salt water in the form of a convex lens. As densities of fresh and sea water are roughly in the ratio of 40:41, the depth of sea water below sea level is 40 times the height of fresh water above sea level. The effect of overpumping near the coast (lower left) is to produce both a cone of depression and a wedge of sea water that rises toward the borehole. If water table finally ceases to slope seaward, or if it drops below sea level, sea water flows landward and contaminates boreholes.

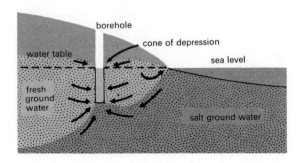

The photograph on the right shows one method of artificially recharging ground water in California. A series of basins are dug parallel to an existing stream on an alluvial plain. Water is led into upper basin by canal, and as this basin fills, it spills into the second, and so on, finally returning to the stream. Silt and algae eventually clog the basins so that filtration stops. Basins are then scraped clean.

In many areas, ground water is artificially recharged for the benefit of water supplies. Where the land is flat, water may be spread in a thin sheet over a large spreading area surrounded by banks or ditches. In alluvial plains a series of shallow basins can be built alongside the river, which is connected to the upper basin by a canal. As the first basin fills, water spills into the second, and so on. Most of the water seeps into the ground, and any excess flows from the lowest basin back into the river. As part of the water supply of Amsterdam and The Hague, water is diverted into basins constructed in coastal sand dunes, which not only help to filter the water but also prevent sea-water intrusion. The main disadvantage of artificial recharge is that the ground surface becomes clogged with silt, algae, or both. It thus becomes necessary to rest the beds for long periods, or to renew the upper layer. In Sweden the water is filtered to speed up recharging—an increasingly common practice in many parts of the world. When an impermeable stratum restricts the flow of water to an aquifer, recharge wells are used to transfer water underground. This action reverses the normal supply well. More than 1100 recharge wells, for example, have been drilled on Long Island, New York, also preventing sea-water intrusion.

Despite frequent mismanagement of ground water, it is fortunately not too late to rectify our mistakes. By applying the results of modern research, we can use existing aquifers more efficiently and develop new ones. More countries will probably adopt the approach of such places as California and Mid Cheshire in the *conjunctive* use of ground and surface water—that is, with ground water kept as a reserve for dry periods. Ground water development on a more intensive scale is likely in the future, even if this sometimes involves artificial recharge. Aquifers are *natural* reservoirs that can be simply tapped by sinking boreholes and pumping water to the surface. *Surface* reservoirs, on the other hand, are costly to build, occupy valuable land, and often involve building long aqueducts. By using aquifers as underground reservoirs, there are no dangers of dam failure, no silting-up of surface reservoirs and—of special importance in hot countries—no wasteful losses by evaporation.

7 Lakes and Reservoirs

The natural fresh-water lakes scattered over the face of the earth benefit man in many different ways. Large lakes are used for transport; others provide electric power. The stillness of their waters allows river sediment to sink to the bottom, leaving the water clearer for water supplies. With their large storage capacity they reduce the flood intensity of the out-flowing river and increase its flow in drought. Many lakes provide fish for recreation and sometimes for a fish industry. They may provide water for irrigation, or become a dump for municipal sewage, like Lake Geneva and some of the Great Lakes of America.

Lakes are born of a variety of natural occurrences. Some of the largest are formed by earth movements. Two examples are Lake Tanganyika, one of the rift valley lakes of Africa, which averages 1650 feet in depth, and Lake Baikal in Russia, which averages 5200 feet in depth. Many deep lakes in the Azores and Iceland are the water-filled craters of extinct volcanoes. Lakes may also form where a glacier blocks a river valley, or where glaciers melt and shed their load of rock as a terminal moraine. This occurred at Windermere in England, and Loch Lomond in Scotland. Landslides, which are a common feature of alpine regions, can form a natural dam across a river valley. In 1840 an earthquake toppled part of the mountain Nanga Parbat (Kashmir) into the Indus River, and produced a lake 40 miles long and 1000 feet deep. Months later the dam gave way, releasing the pent-up waters within 24 hours, with disastrous results. In Japan, as in the Auvergne district of France, lava flows have blocked rivers; Lake Tiberias in Israel was formed in the same way. Deltaic lakes, such as those of the Rhône and Nile deltas, are produced by the building-up of banks of sand and gravel by offshore currents.

Another way in which lakes are made is by erosion. Over long periods, glaciers have eroded U-shaped valleys in the Lake District, Scotland, Norway, and the Himalayas, producing finger lakes. Drift lakes, formed at the end of the ice age after the withdrawal of the ice sheet, are shallow and of irregular outline, and abound in Finland and Canada. Icebergs left by the ice sheet have sunk into soft earth to produce small lakes in Britain and also the Baltic lakes of Denmark and Germany. Other lakes were formed when water dissolved away soluble rocks, as in parts of the Swiss Dolomites.

The composition and concentration of salts and organic matter in lakes and reservoirs are determined by those of their river inflows. The make-up of river water in turn depends on the type of soil over which the water has drained. This drainage area, called the *catchment area*, is separated from neighboring areas by a ridge usually known as a *watershed* (a term also applied to the catchment area, p. 42). Many alpine lakes contain very little organic matter, because soil and vegetation are sparse on their catchment areas. They also contain a very low concentration of salts because they are surrounded by hard insoluble rock. In contrast, limestone and dolomite areas give water a pronounced hardness, while sulfur and other compounds occur in volcanic lakes.

In temperate climates, lakes rarely dry up by evaporation. But in the tropics and subtropics, where the rate of evaporation may exceed the rate of the river inflow, or where there is no outlet, a fresh-water lake may disappear; or it may become very saline, like the Dead Sea. In the tropics, evaporation may exceed 100 inches a year, and if runoff is also low, lake levels can fluctuate by as much as 40 feet.

Drought can also have serious effects outside the tropics. For example, a critical situation

Ullswater (above) is a finger lake in the Lake
District of England. Water flows from the lake through
a gravity aqueduct to Manchester, 90 miles away.

Right: Diagrams show temperature of a typical lake in a temperate climate at different depths in February and July. In winter, the lake has a uniform temperature of 4°C. In summer, it is stratified into three layers: the epilimnion, which is warm and therefore floats on top; the thermocline, where the temperature rapidly changes with depth; and the hypolimnion, a layer of almost uniformly cold water.

The silted-up Mono Reservoir (left) was built as a collecting basin for silt and debris that would otherwise have blocked the main reservoir that supplies Santa Barbara, California. A fire had destroyed large areas of forest in the catchment area. Without the protection of trees, rain washed away large amounts of topsoil.

arose in the Great Lakes at the beginning of the navigation season of the St. Lawrence Seaway in 1964. Water levels were at their lowest point since records began. So serious was the position in Montreal harbor that ships had to reduce their draft by loading 10,800 tons of grain instead of 16,800.

Until recently it was thought that planting forests (*reforestation*) on catchment areas helped to conserve water. A few people even claimed that trees actually increased rainfall. Admittedly, reforestation often reduces soil erosion, especially on steep slopes, and so prevents lakes and reservoirs from silting up. Forests also reduce the intensity of peak floods by moderating runoff. Today there are second thoughts as to whether reforestation is the right policy in all cases. Trees, especially conifers, intercept on their leaves a large proportion of the rainfall, which then evaporates instead of reaching the ground. Runoff, and the replenishment of aquifers by the downward infiltration of water through the soil, may therefore actually be reduced by reforestation. But the effects of forests on runoff and infiltration, the interception of rain by leaves, and evaporation, are very complex factors. Each catchment area must be considered individually before deciding whether more is to be gained by planting or by cutting down various types of plant cover.

In terms of geological time, lakes are a very transient feature of the earth's surface. During their brief existence, they are constantly changing. Inflowing streams deposit sediment in deltaic fashion into the calm, shallow upstream end of the lake. Simultaneously, the outlet stream gradually cuts deeper into the natural barrier holding back the water. The lake level slowly falls until, choked by weed, silt, and vegetation, the lake becomes marshland. Biologically, it has reached its richest state on the borderline between the two great systems of land and water. To the naturalist, this aged specimen has a new value as a wetland teeming with life (Chapter 8). But the lake is dead to the engineer, the economist, and the planner.

The physical, chemical, and biological changes that take place in lakes and reservoirs are so important that a whole science has grown up around them, called *limnology*. These changes depend very much on the size of a lake and on the climate. But the basic principles are best shown by considering a large, deep lake—such as Lake Michigan—where there is a very cold winter and a hot summer. Suppose we start in the autumn, when the lake is cooling rapidly. As the surface water cools, its density increases, the water sinks, and is replaced by warmer water from below. This process continues until the whole lake has cooled to 4°C.—the temperature at which water's density is greatest (p. 17). Because the whole lake has the same density, it

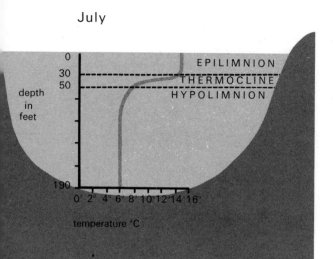

July

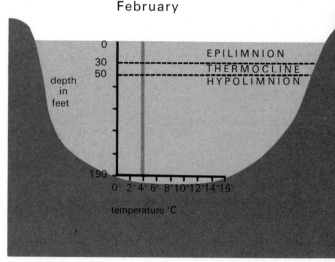

February

then circulates freely under the influence of the autumn winds.

When the air temperature falls to below 4°c., the upper layer of water decreases in density and so remains at the surface. With a hard frost, a layer of ice up to two feet thick may form at the surface. The ice floats on the water beneath, which has a temperature above freezing point. This curious relation between water's temperature and density, which we discussed in Chapter 1, is one of the happiest peculiarities in nature. Without it, the lake could freeze from the bottom upward, destroying all life in the process.

During the winter, water immediately beneath the ice cools down to near freezing point, but water in the deeper parts remains at 4°c. When, in the spring, the days become longer and warmer, the ice melts and the surface water soon warms up to 4°c. The whole lake is again almost uniform in density, and a slight wind is enough to circulate the water. As spring proceeds, the surface water warms up, becomes less dense than the water beneath, and so forms a distinct layer, or *epilimnion*, which may be as deep as 30 feet. Below, there is a zone a few feet thick where the temperature rapidly changes. This zone is called the *thermocline*, and the cool, static water trapped beneath is called the *hypolimnion*.

During the winter, as we saw, the lake is *stratified*, with ice and the coldest water at the surface. In summer, the lake is again stratified,

but the other way round, with the warmest water at the top. During summer, water in the epilimnion is circulated by winds, and warm inflowing streams add to its depth. The hypolimnion is unaffected by the sun or winds, and remains cold.

In spring, increased light and heat encourage the growth of dormant algae in the epilimnion. These multiply very quickly, and the dead algae are heavy enough to penetrate the thermocline and sink into the hypolimnion. By midsummer, the epilimnion still has plenty of oxygen, but has run short of nutrients. The growth of algae then slows down considerably and many species die. In the hypolimnion the dissolved oxygen is soon consumed in breaking down the dead algae. The process of decay is then taken over by anaerobic organisms (see p. 32), which produce obnoxious compounds such as hydrogen sulfide, soluble iron salts, and methane. When this happens, only the epilimnion is fit to be used in water systems. The stratified condition persists until autumn, when the cooling of the surface water causes the whole lake to turn over. The upper layers are again charged with nutrients to provide for algal growth the following year. If there has been a large amount of anaerobic decay during the summer, the autumn mixing means that waterworks are unable to use water from any level of the lake until the products of decay are oxidized.

Such is the broad outline of the seasonal behavior of a lake, but there are many variations. In temperate climates, seasonal changes differ from the situation in Lake Michigan only in so far as a lake may not reach 4°C. throughout. But there is still an autumn mixing as soon as the epilimnion cools to the same temperature as the hypolimnion. In the tropics, many lakes are stratified all the year round, with an epilimnion permanently deficient in nutrients and with a hypolimnion highly charged with nutrients. Such lakes are poor producers of plankton and fish. The only time when the upper layer contains nutrients is after a high wind has driven the epilimnion to one end, exposing the hypolimnion at the other. Then surges of water between gusts cause some mixing of the two layers at the wind-ward end of the lake.

Thermal stratification in upland lakes and reservoirs is usually unimportant, because inflowing streams contain little organic and inorganic matter to support algae. Lowland water, on the other hand, is usually polluted with minerals and organic matter from industrial and domestic effluents. Such water provides an ideal breeding ground for algae, which may later clog filter beds and make the water taste and smell.

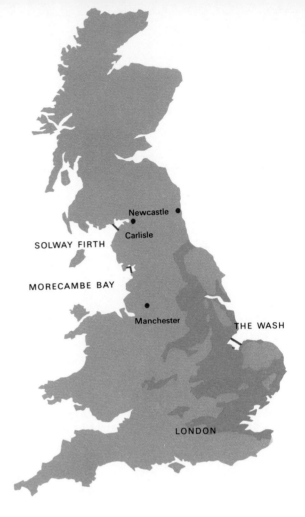

These pages illustrate various types of reservoirs. Above: Barrages, or low dams (red) that would convert three English sea inlets to fresh-water reservoirs. Sluice gates in the barrages would open at low tide to allow excess fresh water to flow through. The gates would shut at high tide to prevent entry of sea water. The Northwest of England's expanding population and industry are badly in need of more water. The rapidly developing Southeast would also benefit from such projects, especially as large areas (blue) have only about 25 inches of rain a year, and farmers have insufficient water in nine years out of ten.

Lake Bala, Wales (above left), is a river-regulating reservoir. Water is abstracted from the river about 25 miles downstream. The reservoir simply adds water to the low river flow during drought.

The Queen Mary Reservoir (left) is one of several large storage reservoirs that receive water from the Thames River. It provides a reserve for dry periods and assists in reducing sediment and bacteria.

The need for more water and the rising cost of land both encourage the construction of deeper storage reservoirs, at least 100 feet deep. In the past, two objections were raised against deep reservoirs. First, the hypolimnion would be deoxygenated and therefore useless just when the summer demand reached its peak. Secondly, the reservoir would be unusable during the autumn overturn, when the polluted hypolimnion would contaminate the epilimnion.

Today, these objections no longer apply, because there are now ways of preventing stratification, such as introducing water into reservoirs at high velocity to cause turbulence and mixing. Another method is to use a vertical air-lift pump, which continuously lifts water from the hyoplimnion into the epilimnion. The "aerohydraulic gun," for instance, consists of a plastic tube that discharges a compressed-air bubble that entraps water as it rises. It is a cheap and effective device with low maintenance costs. It also requires very little power because the transference of water beneath the surface requires very little energy.

The flow of most rivers fluctuates widely from season to season; in North Africa many of them dry up completely every summer. The maximum amount that can be used for water supplies throughout the year is determined by the minimum flow, called the *dry-weather flow*. Surplus water during wet periods is wasted unless it is stored in reservoirs. A reservoir is simply an artificial lake, or· "water bank." It may be a natural lake whose outlet has been dammed so that the water level can be adjusted. Alternatively, a completely new lake may be formed by damming a river valley. In the few places where the river flow is uniform, as when it is fed by an ample spring, reservoirs are unnecessary. Nor are reservoirs needed in areas, such as a village on the Amazon, where water requirements are only a small fraction of the dry-weather flow of the river. But as more and more water is taken from a river, so the risk of it drying up in drought increases and the need for a reservoir grows.

The traditional type of reservoir—which also produces the cleanest water—is made by building a dam across a relatively uninhabited upland valley. Another type occurs at Plover Cove, Hong Kong, for example, where a sea inlet is being converted to hold fresh water running down from the hills by building a dam across the inlet. Similar projects are being considered in England. Another type of reservoir is formed on

Left: A London service reservoir in the process of being covered in the 1850's. A recent act had enforced the covering of all service reservoirs to prevent germs, algae, and dirt from polluting the filtered water. Service reservoirs are so elevated that water flows to homes and buildings by gravity and at the correct pressure. Where no ground at the correct elevation exists a water tower (right) is built instead.

flat land by an encircling embankment to receive water pumped from a nearby river. This type of reservoir is particularly useful when upland sites are distant, as in the case of London. One of the most efficient types of reservoir is that used for river regulation, where a reservoir on the headwaters both supplements the flow of the river in drought and acts as a retention basin during winter floods.

The economics of reservoir design are governed by two extremes: the dry-weather flow of the river, and the intensity of the anticipated peak floods. These extremes are worked out from meteorological records covering a period of at least 20 years, and are best recorded on an automatic gauge across the river. From these readings it is possible to estimate statistically the likely intensity of a drought or flood at intervals of, say, 20, 50, 100, or 1000 years. Much more difficult to decide is what intensity of extremes the reservoir and dam should be designed to meet. Obviously the once-in-a-hundred-years drought is far more severe than the once-in-ten-years, and far more costly to allow for. In some parts of the world it would be impractical to allow for every eventuality. On the island of Mauritius, for example, the prospect always exists of the top layer of water being blown out of the reservoir by a hurricane at the beginning of the dry season. Another problem for water engineers is the amount of room that should be allowed in a reservoir for silting. The life-span of a reservoir may vary from 20 years in some parts of Bolivia or India to 800 years in the few silt-free drainage areas of Western Europe. With all these variables to consider, any estimate of the safe yield of a reservoir can only be approximate. It is not surprising that some reservoirs periodically go dry, or that dams occasionally give way under exceptional floods.

The creation of reservoirs in bare river valleys involves no actual construction work on the valley basin itself. All that has to be done is to clear away vegetation and rehouse the valley population. The really difficult and costly part of any reservoir project is building the dam and its foundations. Men have been building dams for over 5000 years. At first these were laid across the beds of small streams, sometimes to be swept away with the next flood, at other times to last for many centuries. Most of these early dams were built to store water for irrigation and drinking, although some were made to trap fish, otters, beavers, and other animals. The oldest dam in existence stands in the eastern desert of Egypt across the Wadi Gerrawi. (A wadi is a watercourse that is dry most of the year, but briefly carries floodwater.) Made of rough masonry 3000 years ago, it once stored the brief winter rains to supply workers in the nearby alabaster quarries. Around 1300 B.C., the Lake of Homs in Syria, 20 square miles in area, was formed by the Orontes Dam, whose sluices still supply the neighboring irrigation canals. Many ancient dams still exist in Arabia, the most notable near Marib in the Yemen, of fine masonry keyed together with copper fastenings. The Romans built many large masonry dams in Italy and North Africa from which water flowed to cities along aqueducts. In the Middle East, cement-lined tanks and stone cisterns abound; one at Aden has a capacity of over 36 MG. The Israel coast is still dotted with Roman cisterns that were constructed to collect some of the expected annual 56 days of rain.

Now scientifically designed, modern dams approach heights of 800 feet. It is perhaps difficult to appreciate that large dams are among the most costly of all engineering projects. Large dams contain an enormous amount of material. The Hoover dam, which stores the entire flow of the Colorado River for two years, is as high as a 60-story skyscraper. The Grand Coulee Dam, with a waterfall over its spillway more than twice as high as the Niagara Falls, contains enough concrete to build a highway across the United States and back.

Water-supply dams collect water for domestic and industrial use for cities like New York, Los

Top: This dam across a river was made by beavers. Other natural barriers that cause a build-up of water result from landslides, glaciers, and accumulated driftwood. It was probably by observing such phenomena that early man was inspired to make artificial dams.

Bottom: This Roman dam across a wadi in the Syrian desert once helped to collect the winter rains. The dam is now obsolete; in any case it could no longer function because the wadi behind it has silted up. Sooner or later, modern dams will suffer the same fate.

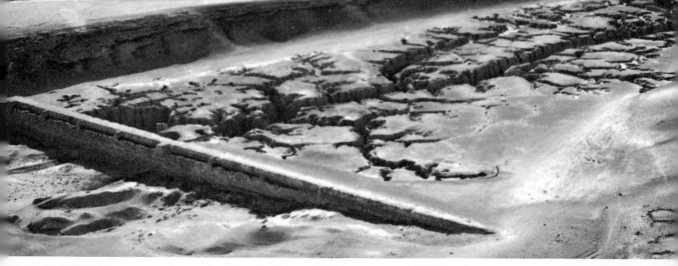

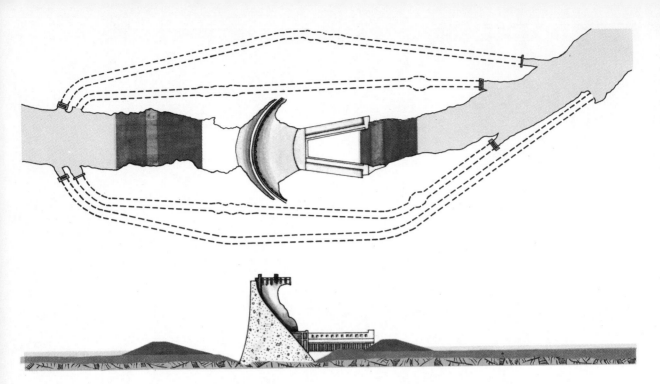

Top: One stage in the construction of the Hoover Dam. First, there was much preliminary work, including building a town to house personnel for 7 years. Four 50-foot-diameter diversion tunnels (dotted lines), with a total length of 3 miles, were then excavated in the volcanic sides of the gorge. The Colorado River was held back from the dam site and diverted through these tunnels by two cofferdams (brown), made by dumping rock across the river. Above: Cross-section of the dam.

Left: The completed dam. It is a gravity arch type and the highest (726 feet) in the world. It was built out of massive blocks of concrete in which were embedded 580 miles of steel tube through which a coolant was pumped to remove the excessive heat produced by the setting concrete. It would have taken a century for the blocks to cool naturally, during which time the concrete would have shrunk and produced dangerous cracks in the dam. When the blocks had set, the gaps between them were grouted (p. 90) to form a single structure. Both diversion tunnels were then plugged at (a). Two spillways, built in the sides of the gorge, now lead excess floodwater to shafts connected with the lower part of the outer diversion tunnel. Intake towers (b) lead water to penstocks and then to a powerhouse at the base of the dam.

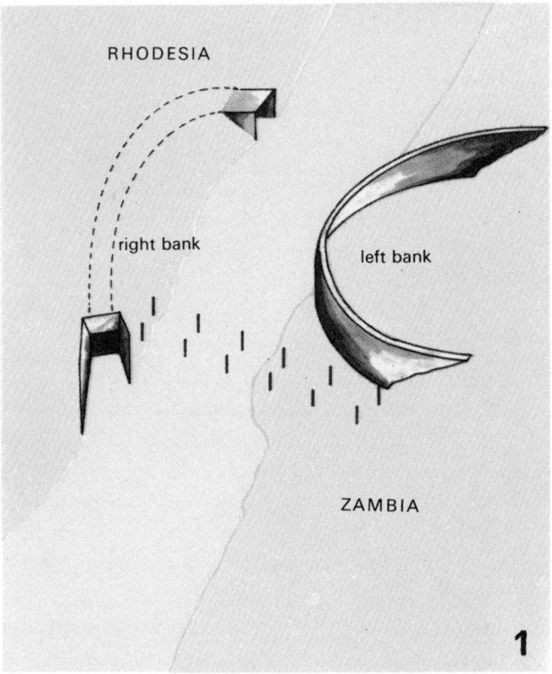

Diagrams on this page show stages in the construction of the Kariba hydroelectric dam, Africa. The arch, or curved, dam is 460 feet high and only 80 feet thick; a gravity type would have had to be 280 feet thick at the base. (1) Diversion channel and curved cofferdam built on left bank, and a diversion tunnel on right bank.
(2) Left flank of main dam, with temporary openings, constructed inside cofferdam; right flank built above floodwater level. Two bridges completed. Work started on power station, which, because of lack of room in gorge, was underground.
(3) Cofferdam demolished to let water through diversion channel and gaps in main dam. A rock-fill cofferdam built to force water through diversion channel and tunnel. Two curved cofferdams built between flanks of main dam, inside which right flank of main dam was completed.
(4) Diversion tunnel and openings of left flank closed in order to impound water in reservoir. The dam was raised. Power station and intakes (dotted lines) completed. Water started to pass through tunnel intake to turbines connected to electric generators.
(5) The completed dam. Six spillways take the form of chutes through the dam.

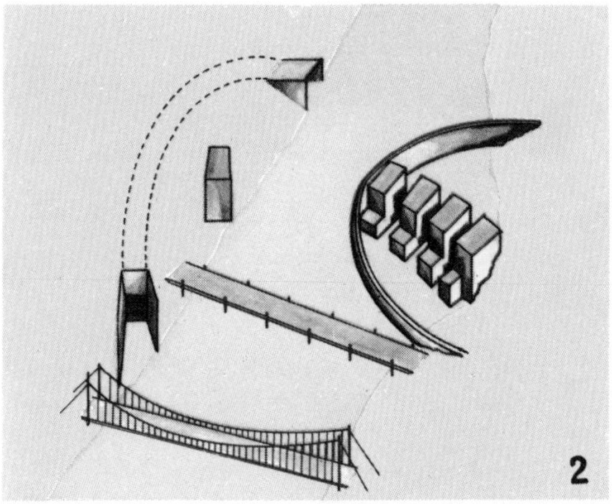

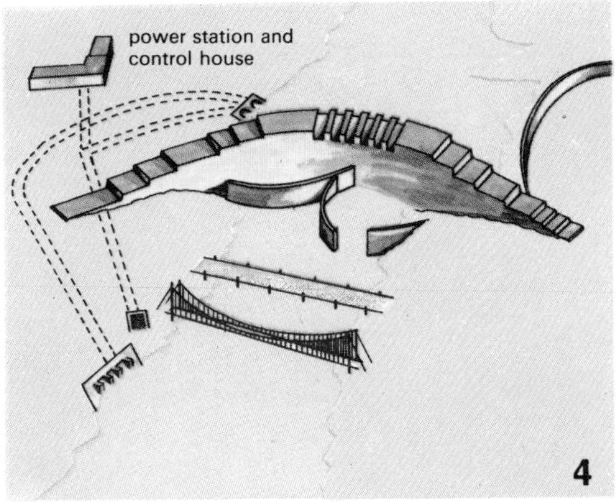

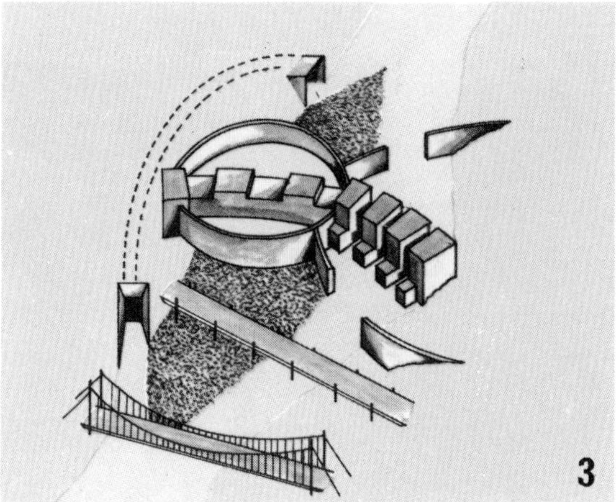

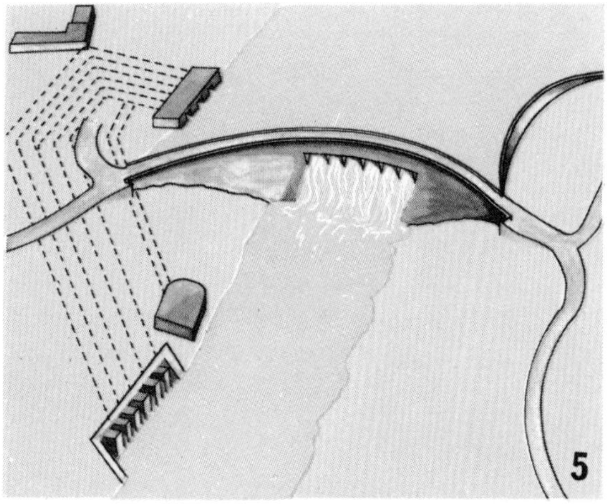

Angeles, and Manchester (England). Flood-control dams are essential in some parts of the world to save lives and property, such as the five dams of the Miami River valley, which protect Dayton, Ohio. Navigation dams, usually consisting of a stairlike series of dams and locks, are built to maintain a minimum depth of water for ships.

Irrigation dams are a common feature in arid areas such as India and Pakistan. Irrigation is also the primary function of the Hoover Dam. Before it was built, the Colorado River flooded the Imperial Valley in Arizona when the mountain snows melted, and became a sluggish stream in summer. Now the reservoir saves the floodwater and has greatly increased the irrigated area. The Grand Coulee Dam on the Columbia River was built partly because the river had cut its bed too deep. From the reservoir created by the dam, large pumps lift water to another reservoir on the plateau, to supply farms through a canal system.

A very important irrigation dam is the Aswan High Dam, started in Egypt in 1960, near the old Aswan Dam built in 1902. Half of Egypt's population are farmers who rely entirely on irrigation. In the past they produced only one crop a year, by the old system of basin irrigation. After the new dam is built, there will be sufficient water for several crops a year, and the irrigated land will be increased by 1.7 million acres. It will also produce 2100 megawatts of electric power. Virtually a rainless country, Egypt depends for its existence entirely on the Nile, the second longest river in the world. In summer, the Nile's flow, increased by monsoon runoff from the Abyssinian highlands, floods large areas of the adjacent land. Formerly, most of this summer floodwater drained into the sea, and about once every decade, disastrous floods destroyed agricultural land and canals. The Aswan High Dam will create a giant lake, 315 miles long and an average 5 miles in width, to store this surplus water from one year to the next. One-quarter of its capacity will be reserved to accommodate the freak floods, while a small fraction will accommodate the silt carried by the Nile.

Hydroelectric power dams use the force of falling water to move turbine blades connected with an electric generator. The turbines and generators are housed in a power station in or below the dam, or in a diversion tunnel in the valley side. The amount of electricity produced depends on both the pressure and the volume of the water. One of the most important African hydroelectric projects is the Volta Dam in Ghana, completed in 1965. Ghana had relied on cocoa and gold for most of its income, but in 1952 President Nkrumah decided to expand the economy by creating industries. Since industries require power, hitherto obtained from expensive imported diesel oil, it was decided to use the Volta River to produce 512,000 kilowatts of electricity. Of this, 60 per cent would be used for a new aluminum smelter, and the remainder for domestic use and for future industries.

Since the flow of the Volta River during the dry season is 300 times less than during flood, it was necessary to create an enormous dam, to form in 1965 the largest man-made lake in the world—3275 square miles in area and 250 miles long. Apart from its main function of providing power, the Volta project also serves other purposes. It provides a cheap means of transport, opening up new opportunities for developing the natural iron deposits and other industries to the north. Because 600 square miles of the lake shore will flood seasonally, new farming communities will be established to grow rice and other crops. Other communities around the lake margin will be able to catch an estimated 11,200 tons of fish a year. The whole project, although dramatic, is based on sound principles. Whether the country can afford to repay the borrowed $170 million, only time will show.

Strange as it may seem, water provides the only economical means of "storing" electrical energy for use at times of peak demand. In *pumped storage* projects, surplus electricity from the grid is used to pump water into higher reservoirs, from which it is released during the day to produce hydroelectric power and augment existing power supplies.

The greatest benefit is invariably obtained from those water projects that serve several purposes. Such *multipurpose* reservoirs may provide any combination of the following services: hydroelectric power, water supply, irrigation, flood control, navigation, fishing, and recreation. One might expect that these different objectives would at times conflict, but in practice this seldom happens.

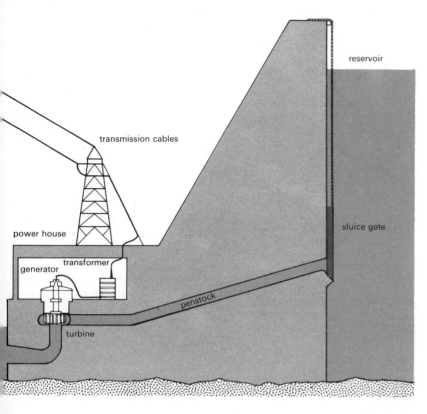

transmission cables

reservoir

power house

sluice gate

transformer

generator

penstock

turbine

Left: Section of a hydroelectric dam. Water passes at high pressure through dam to powerhouse, and drives turbines coupled to electric generators. In some projects, water passes through a tunnel *around* the dam to a power-house that is in the valley below or underground. A minor part of the world's electricity is generated by water power.

Pumped-water storage is the only way of "storing" large quantities of electricity at reasonable cost. In this project in Wales (below), surplus electricity from the grid is used during off-peak hours to pump water from a lower reservoir (extreme right) to the main reservoir. During peak periods, water flows back through turbines to lower reservoir, generating electricity.

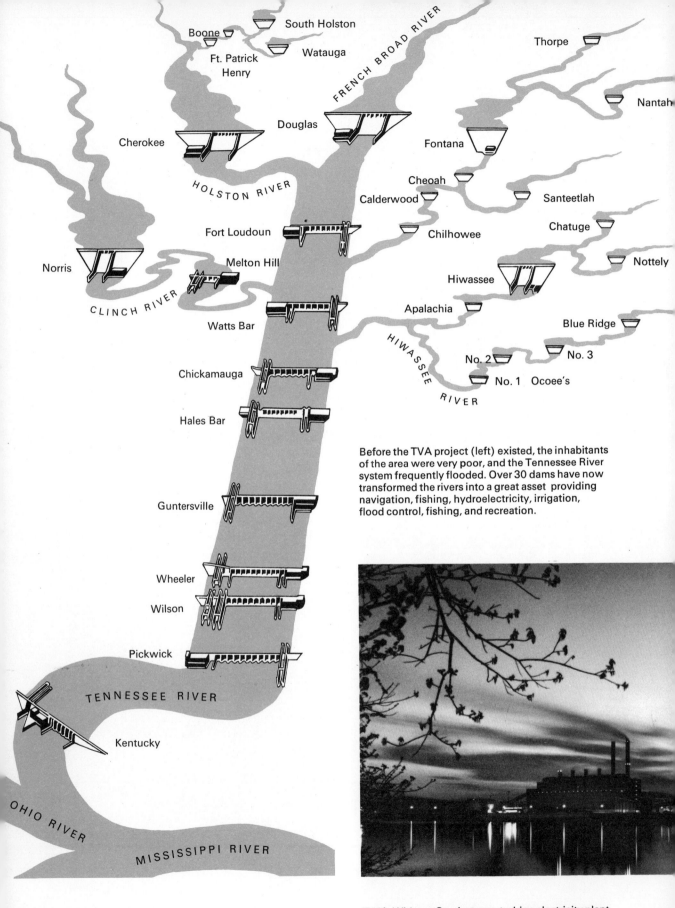

Boone
South Holston
FRENCH BROAD RIVER
Thorpe
Ft. Patrick
Henry
Watauga
Nantah
Douglas
Cherokee
Fontana
Cheoah
Santeetlah
Calderwood
HOLSTON RIVER
Chilhowee
Chatuge
Fort Loudoun
Nottely
Melton Hill
Hiwassee
Norris
CLINCH RIVER
Apalachia
Blue Ridge
Watts Bar
HIWASSEE
No. 2
No. 3
Chickamauga
No. 1
Ocoee's
RIVER
Hales Bar

Before the TVA project (left) existed, the inhabitants of the area were very poor, and the Tennessee River system frequently flooded. Over 30 dams have now transformed the rivers into a great asset providing navigation, fishing, hydroelectricity, irrigation, flood control, fishing, and recreation.

Guntersville

Wheeler

Wilson

Pickwick

TENNESSEE RIVER

Kentucky

OHIO RIVER

MISSISSIPPI RIVER

TVA's Widows Creek steam-turbine electricity plant (above) is the largest in the United States. The plant burns daily about 20,000 tons of coal. It could not exist without taking about one million gallons of cooling water a day from Lake Guntersville.

88

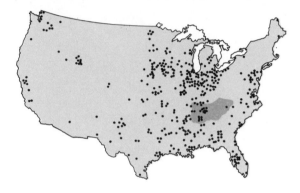

After the TVA began to supply hydroelectric power, several fertilizer plants developed, of which the one illustrated (top) is the largest in the United States. Above: The map shows the area benefited by TVA (dark green) and regions (black dots) where the fertilizers are used.

The first multipurpose project, started during the great American depression of the 1930's, was created by the Tennessee Valley Authority (TVA) to develop the poverty-stricken Tennessee basin. Most of the population were farmers who had to contend with bad soil fertility and erosion as well as a river too shallow for navigation in summer and liable to violent flooding in winter.

Today there are 31 large and 12 small dams along 650 miles of the river and its tributaries. The lake levels are kept low just before the winter floods, during which as much water as possible is allowed to discharge past the dams. After the flood season ends, the reservoirs fill up with the spring rains. During summer and autumn this water is released to maintain an adequate river flow, leaving the lake levels low again for the start of the next winter floods. The TVA project produced a notable rise in the region's standard of living and agriculture. Flood control alone saves about $520 million annually. The project also provides large amounts of hydroelectric power for industrial and domestic use. The dams and locks have turned the river into a navigable stairway of lakes—a great advantage to the many new industries. There are also 50 times more fish than there were before, providing new opportunities for recreation.

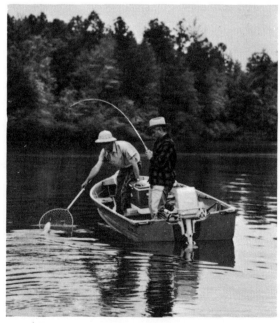

Game fishing (above) is an important side-effect afforded by the TVA project, but a considerable amount of commercial fishing is also practiced. About 12,000 tons of fish are caught each year in the region for the commercial market.

The principles involved in building dams will be more easily grasped with the help of the diagrams. A dam must be strong enough to withstand the tremendous force of water pushing against its walls. Contrary to what one might expect, this force has no relation to the length of the reservoir. For the same depth of water and area of dam exposed, the water pressure is exactly the same in a reservoir 10 miles long as it is in one of 100 miles. The horizontal thrust on a dam depends solely on the depth of water, increasing by 624 pounds per square foot for every ten-foot increase in depth. The force is therefore greatest at the *base* of the dam. In a reservoir 100 feet deep, this will be 3.1 ton per square foot, and a dam 100 feet high and a half mile long will have to sustain a total water pressure of 394,000 tons. There is thus a tendency for the whole structure to be pushed downstream, and also for it to be tipped over (illus. opposite). Such tendencies are usually counteracted by making the dam broadest at the base, and sufficiently heavy. Excessive pressure on the dam during floods is prevented by building a *spillway*, which may take the form of a diversion tunnel through or around the dam. A spillway may also simply be a chute over the *crest*.

If there is leakage under the dam, another force comes into play that tends to lift the dam off its foundations. Such seepage is prevented by building a *cutoff wall* from the dam down to impermeable bedrock. If the dam already rests on firm rock, any rock cracks are filled up by injecting liquid cement—a process called *grouting*. It is also important to prevent leakage through the dam itself, not so much to prevent the escape of water as to prevent the stability of the structure from being undermined. Waterproofing is achieved by having an impervious center (*core*) or an impervious upstream face.

Several factors have to be considered before deciding what type of dam to build, where it should be sited, and how much margin of safety there should be. Wrong decisions have led to

Right: Diagram summarizes the three main forces on dams. The two forces P and U tend to turn dam around imaginary hinge, X, and act against weight of dam, W, which tends to keep it stable. Much research is done before construction starts, to ensure that P plus U do not exceed W.

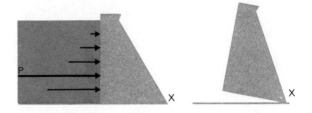

Since water pressure increases by 624 lb/sq ft for every 10-foot increase in depth, the deeper the reservoir the greater the force on the dam (above). The force on the vertical face is equivalent to a single force, P, acting at a third of the depth from the bottom. If this force is too great, dam turns about the downstream toe, X. This turning effect is counteracted by making the dam sufficiently heavy and broad at the base. The force P also tends to push the whole dam downstream. This is prevented by having ridges on the dam base that fit into troughs in the foundations.

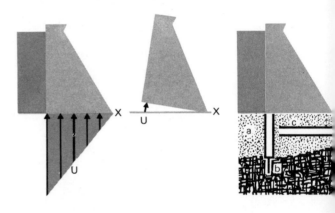

A little water seeps under the base of most dams (above) and causes an uplift pressure, U, that tends to turn the dam about its downstream toe, X. The uplift is proportional to the depth of water. In the past, about half of dam failures were due to uplift. This is now counteracted by building a cutoff wall (a) from the upstream face of the dam (where uplift is greatest) down to firm, impermeable bedrock. Liquid cement, called grout (b), is also injected into cracks and fissures in the bedrock to make foundations watertight. Drainage holes (c), downstream of the cutoff wall, help to reduce the accumulation of water.

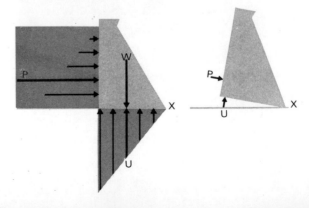

The spillways of Kariba Dam (above) are six chutes *through* the dam. The bellmouth spillway (top) diverts flood-water *around* dam into the downstream channel. Inadequate spillways account for over 20 per cent of past dam failures. The tilting effect on a dam is proportional to the cube of the depth. Suppose a dam was built to withstand a 10-foot rise above normal in a 100-foot-deep reservoir. Then suppose the level rose 30 feet because of an inadequate spillway. The tilting force would be $(130/110)^3 = 1.6$. The extra force (0.6) would overturn many dams.

disasters in the past, so today great care is taken to make a proper preliminary investigation. This starts with a geological survey to determine whether the rock foundations are strong and stable enough to take the weight of the dam without shifting later. The choice of dam also depends on the nature of the available materials. As the movement of material, sometimes involving shifting 10 million tons, forms a large proportion of the total cost, materials are usually used from the immediate neighborhood.

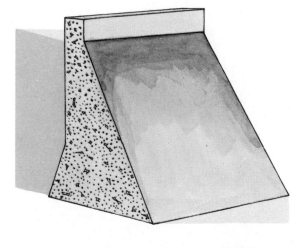

The most permanent dam, and the one that requires least maintenance, is the *solid gravity concrete dam*. So long as the underlying rock can withstand the enormous weight of these massive structures, this kind of dam can be built almost anywhere and can be made much higher than those of earth or rock. The spillway usually takes the form of a chute over the crest. If the dam is used for hydroelectric power, water passes to the powerhouse either through the dam or through a diversion tunnel at the side. In other cases, large pipes called *penstocks* convey water from the dam to the powerhouse.

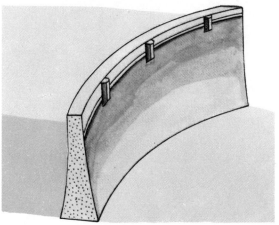

In the few sites where there is a narrow gorge with strong sides, a curved concrete wall can be built so that the force of water is transferred to the cliff sides. Such a *curved dam*, or *arch dam*, unlike a solid gravity concrete dam, relies for stability on its shape, rather than on its weight. It also contains much less concrete and so is cheaper to construct. The greatest stability is achieved when the gorge is narrow and deep, and the thinner the dam the more it depends on the strength of the gorge sides. For this reason, thin arch dams need to be very carefully designed.

In a wide valley a concrete *multiple arch*, or *buttress*, *dam* may be built. This type is really a modification of the curved dam, and consists of a series of short arches supported by buttresses. The arches slope at an angle of about 45° on the upstream face, so that water bears down on the dam and helps to give it stability. Sometimes flat slabs of reinforced concrete are used instead of arches.

Left: A typical solid gravity dam. It is always made of concrete or masonry, and resists water pressure by weight alone. It costs more than rock or earth dams, but can be built to a greater height—that is, if the foundations can bear the enormous weight. Right: A solid gravity dam used by the Birmingham Water Works, England. Floodwater pours over the spillway crest.

Left: A typical arch, or curved, dam. This type is always made of concrete and can be built only in narrow gorges. It relies mainly on its shape, rather than on its weight, for stability—transmitting the water pressure to the gorge sides by thrust. The Hoover Dam (right) is a combined curved and gravity type, using both arch action and weight for stability.

A multiple arch, or buttress, dam (left) consists of many short arches supported by triangular buttresses. Sometimes flat slabs are used instead of arches. This type of concrete dam is a modification of the curved dam in that it resists water pressure by arch action, but stability is enhanced by having the upstream face inclined at about 45° so that water presses down on the dam. Right: An Italian multiple arch dam.

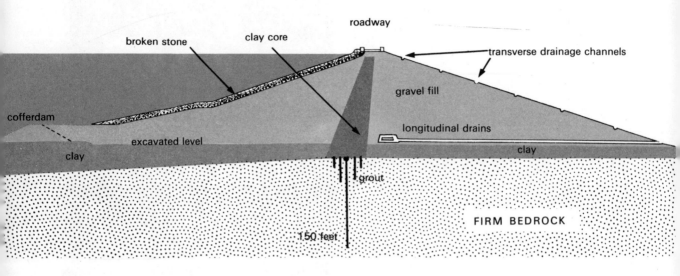

Above: Cross-section of the Tryweryn earth dam, Wales. A waterproof core of compressed clay reaches down to bedrock and extends into the bedrock as a grout curtain. The upstream and downstream shoulders are made of gravel although some early earth dams were made entirely of clay. The photograph (right, above) of Tryweryn Dam shows the great width compared with the height. The upstream face is covered with stones to prevent erosion by waves. The downstream face is turfed and has transverse drainage channels to prevent erosion by rain.

The *earth dam*, made of sand, gravel, or clay, is practical only if these materials are near at hand. Since they have a very broad base, earth dams are particularly suitable where the valley floor is too soft to bear the weight of a concrete dam. They are also fairly flexible, and so are suitable in places where gradual earth movements are likely to occur. Earth dams contain a waterproof core reaching from ground to above high-water level, supported on either side with earth. Puddle clay is often used for the core, but in dry countries like South Africa, parts of America, and Australia, the core is made of less flexible but stronger concrete. The core is invariably taken down into the bedrock as a concrete cutoff wall. The downstream slope of the dam is protected from erosion by heavy rain with gravel or turf. The upstream slope is protected from wave action by rock or concrete slabs. Unlike the tougher concrete dams, the spillway of an earth dam is always separated from the dam itself in a special overflow leading to a tunnel cut into the side of the valley. Water pouring over the crest would destroy the downstream face. This most ancient of all types of dam has become increasingly common during the last 30 years. While concrete dams remain relatively the same in price, earth dams have become cheaper and more reliable because of advances in the science of soil mechanics and better earth-moving machinery. Well-designed earth dams also require very little maintenance.

The *rock dam* is another ancient type that is becoming more popular. It is built in places where suitable rock can be quarried near the site—particularly in canyons, where rock is first dumped into the river. The upstream face is covered with carefully graded rock, and then faced with concrete to resist seepage and wave action. Sometimes an inner waterproof soil core is used, as in the High Aswan and Volta dams. Rock dams cannot withstand earth movements as well as soil dams, and because of their open texture they need a spillway around the dam.

Right and below: Diagram and photograph of the Volta rockfill dam in Ghana, Africa. Like the earth dam, it is very broad at the base. It is made waterproof with a clay core, and the cofferdams have been retained to form the upstream and downstream toes.

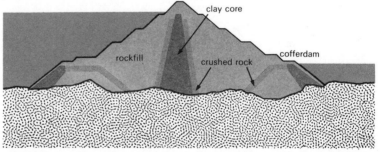

clay core

rockfill

crushed rock

cofferdam

Public safety first and economics second dictate the choice of dam. Every effort must be taken to ensure sound foundations, even settlement, adequate spillways, and good-quality materials. Some dams now approach the 800-foot-high mark, holding back masses of water unheard of years ago. The benefits are great—the potential dangers sometimes greater, if the designer has miscalculated the forces at work. At Fréjus in France, the failure of an arch dam in 1959 caused $56 million of damage, and the loss of hundreds of lives. The rock foundations were said to be suitable for a curved dam thick enough to cover the supporting rock, which was not homogeneous. André Coyne, the greatest dam designer the world had ever seen, produced instead a thin arch dam. A few days before the Fréjus tragedy he wrote of his complete faith in his dam: "Each successful experiment is valuable; if it fails, its value is greater."

Reservoirs are so useful that we tend to forget that they can also be a potential menace. Few realize the fury of unleashed water. Water flowing at about 10 miles an hour can roll 10-foot-diameter boulders along a riverbed with ease. Imagine therefore the power of the torrent pouring through the gap torn by the "Dam Busters" in the Möhne Dam, Germany, during World War II. Water passing through a large hole in a dam 100 feet below the surface would in theory travel at nearly 60 miles an hour, a terrifying speed. With 100 million tons of water behind it, this would cause catastrophic destruction in the towns below.

Yet nature has long been an old hand at the game of dam busting. From early times alpine herdsmen have observed a dam produced by a glacier lifting and thus releasing the water stored in the lake behind. In 1934 the Nevado Glacier, blocking the Rio Plonio valley in the Argentine, suddenly floated and let loose 17 billion gallons. An earthquake in Chile in 1960 caused a landslide that blocked the outlet of Lake Rinihue, raising the water level 86 feet and the total storage to 960 billion gallons. Fortunately the perilous situation was relieved by cutting an escape channel before the natural dam burst.

Landslides are common in steep mountainous areas, where some of the best waters and best dam sites are found. In the Piave valley of Italy, on October 9, 1963, there was a night of terror. Within a few seconds 1 billion tons of Mount Toc fell into the newly built Vaiont Reservoir. This pushed a great wave over the new arch dam and swept 2000 villagers to their doom. But the dam remained intact under pressures far greater than those provided for.

A landslide had occurred while the dam was being built, so model tests were made to assess the chances of this happening again. Beneath the limestone of Mount Toc were hard layers of clay, which softened by the penetration of the rising waters of the new reservoir so that the overlying rock slipped. Some authorities claim that the tests were inadequate; others say they were disregarded by the engineers. In any case, such disasters do stress the special responsibility of the dam designer and the necessity of carefully integrating the structure of the dam with the geology of the whole valley.

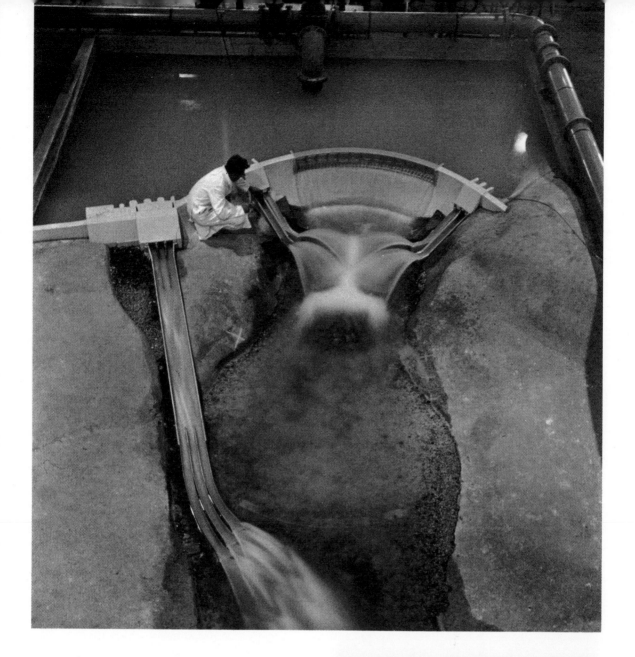

The two photographs on this page show models of the
Van Der Kloof Dam, Orange River Project, South Africa.
They were built by the Hydraulics Research Station,
Wallingford, England. When a detailed appraisal of
a dam's stability in relation to its foundations
cannot be worked out on paper, accurate models are
made as a safety precaution. These particular models
were built to investigate the effect of floodwater
flowing through spillways on scouring of the riverbed below the dam. The early model (right) produced
deep scouring .The final design (above) incorporated
a long sluice to lead water toward a less vulnerable
part of the riverbed.

The photograph (left) of a village wrecked by the
Vaiont Dam disaster in Italy, 1963, portrays the
devastating effect of a sudden flood. A landslide
pushed a giant wave over the arch dam, killing
more than 2000 people in the valley below.

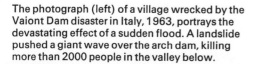

8 Wetlands

Regions that are covered permanently or for long periods with shallow water are known as *wetlands*—a term that includes marshes, swamps, fens, and shallow lakes. The existence of many wetlands is very precarious. Some disappear relatively quickly and become dry land. Others, such as those in the Nile Delta, are gradually disappearing beneath the waves because of land subsidence. Wetlands, in fact, are dwindling faster than any other ecological system—a process that man has accelerated during the last century by drainage and reclamation. As a typical example of the rate at which the world's wetlands are diminishing, there are 74 million acres in the United States today, compared with 127 million a century ago.

To many people, wetlands are just wastelands that should be drained or filled in to provide land for agriculture, building, industry, or roads. For others, wetlands have an educational, scientific, or recreational value. The immediate benefits of reclamation, however, are easier to assess in economic terms than the value of leaving them intact. Thus the economist and engineer are generally allowed to have their way. Such a conflict of interests exists, for example, in Florida. Nearly half the state is wetland, including vast areas of cypresses and the largest mangrove swamps in the world. The Everglades between Lake Okeechobee and the sea consists largely of a 70-mile-wide belt of grass interspersed with channels one to four feet deep. This area of 4000 square miles supports some of the most varied animal life in the United States—alligator, deer, panther, bear, snake, heron, ibis, spoonbill, etc., all making the area a tourist attraction.

On the other hand, Florida's main source of income comes from agriculture, on which the northern states depend for early lettuce, tomatoes, and other cash crops. Much of today's fertile land was once wetland that has been drained. This has involved diverting water by canal from Lake Okeechobee to the sea, or into storage reservoirs for irrigation. The Everglades is, consequently, rapidly drying up. The result is that its wildlife is threatened with extinction, its facilities for sport are dwindling, and some of its fisheries put in serious danger.

However, the importance of conserving certain wetlands is being increasingly recognized. For example, many wetlands provide a large flat area over which floods can spread, and so have an obvious economic value. Even numerous small ponds in a catchment area can have an important effect in smoothing out peak floods. Many authorities have found to their cost that destroying wetlands in order to develop a flood plain commercially increases the rate of runoff and the intensity of floods. Other wetlands, such as those of deltas and estuaries, are often the most fertile areas in the world—more productive, acre for acre, than an ordinary wheat field. This is very important in a world that is short of food. Already parts of the East have found it well worthwhile to "farm" fish in special ponds. But the profit of a wheat field is easier to assess than that of a wetland. As yet, few experts have seriously investigated the potential yield of food from these fresh-water areas.

Other benefits of wetlands have also been underestimated until recently. It is now recognized that many ailments are caused or aggravated by boredom and the unrelieved tensions of

Deltas and estuaries are often very fertile wetlands, producing large quantities of protein-rich food. The Colorado delta (top right) was built up from sediment brought down by the river. But the Hoover Dam upstream has been trapping the silt, and there is concern because the delta is receding and the sea threatens to break through and flood the low-lying land. Far right: An aircraft drops young trout into a fresh-water area in Australia. With two-thirds of the world short of protein, increasing efforts are being made to farm fresh-water fish. Wetlands also support birds for hunting (right).

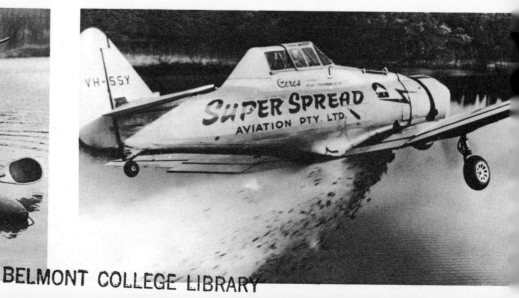

city life. The opportunity for recreation and a change of scene is important, and wetlands provide one of the best places to go. In America, over $3.6 billion are spent every year on fishing for sport and hunting waterfowl. Eighty per cent of American waterfowl breed in the wetlands of Canada, Alaska, and the north-central states of the United States. These birds also spend time in wetlands in the southern United States during migration. There are also a million waterfowl hunters and amateur anglers in Europe, and many of the waterfowl winter in the Camargue wetlands of southern France. Wetlands are also used for scientific and educational study, for they often contain a greater variety and profusion of life than anywhere else. And because wetlands are in a precarious state, often changing rapidly, they provide a valuable opportunity to study the effects of such change on the flora and fauna.

A wise approach seems to be to drain those wetlands that have no great merit, and to leave intact those of exceptional interest. It takes a long time for a wetland to become established. Once destroyed, it can no more be replaced than, say, an historic monument like Abu Simbel in Egypt. And if people can spend enormous sums of money on rescuing Abu Simbel from the rising waters of the Aswan Lake, surely they can leave an interesting wetland alone.

Below: A typical Everglades scene. Above: The great white heron, one of the animals that attract tourists.

The Norfolk Broads (above) is England's principal wetland where over 250,000 people fish, boat, and holiday each year. Below: Wetlands in United States; blue dots show the most important areas.

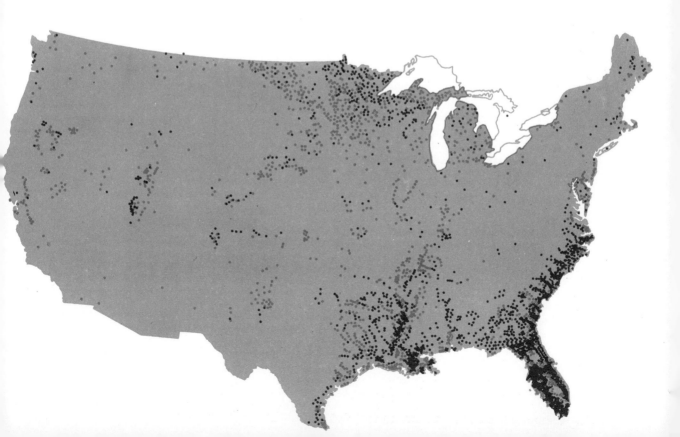

without dikes

1200

1400

1500

1975

Man's greatest success in reclaiming wetlands is the Netherlands, where for centuries people have toiled to convert water to dry land. At one time, the whole of what is now the west of the Netherlands was submerged by the sea. Gradually, however, the winds and tides built up a range of low sand dunes, while silt from the numerous rivers turned the watery stretches behind the dunes into marsh. The Romans, who came to the country around 50 B.C., wrote of a wilderness of marshes and shallow lakes, with a network of rivers, estuaries, and creeks that continually changed their course. At that time the inhabitants lived on mounds of earth built above high-tide level. About the eleventh century, mounds were connected by dikes to enclose land for agriculture.

During the thirteenth century, the sea broke through parts of the coastal sand dunes and flooded large areas of land to form the Zuider Zee. From then on, floods were frequent, and dikes were often breached by heavy seas and high tides. The first dikes were made of earth, and planted with grass to resist erosion from waves. Later, they were strengthened with reeds, straw, and hurdles woven from willows. In the fourteenth century, dikes were constructed of wooden piles backed with compressed seaweed.

Then these were replaced by dikes made of wood. But because these wooden dikes had vertical faces, they broke under severe wave action. In the seventeenth century they were abandoned after they became riddled with holes by a boring mollusk (*Teredo*). After several centuries of dike building, the Dutch learned that the best way to combat wave action is to build sloping dikes faced with stone—a lesson that other countries learned 200 years later after bare-earth dams failed through gradual erosion.

During the seventeenth century, the Dutch started to drain large areas of dike-enclosed land, called *polders*. This was, literally, an uphill task, and they made full use of the only power then available—the windmill. Relays of windmills pumped water from ditch to ditch, to canals, to rivers, and finally into the sea. However, the polders were subsiding, and the Dutch had to heighten hundreds of miles of dikes. Towns like Rotterdam and Amsterdam had to build levees along the river near to where it flowed into the sea to prevent flooding of the land.

In spite of improvements, occasional floods continued well into the twentieth century. After the flood disaster of 1916, the Dutch revived an old plan to eliminate the need for the dikes around the shores of the Zuider Zee ever to be

Right: When a dam across a sea inlet is nearly complete, tidal water rushes through the narrow gap and tends to scour the seabed. Concrete caissons are often used to fill this gap. They are floated into position (note tugboats) and quickly sunk at slack water.

The maps (top left) show the relative extent of dry land (brown) in the Netherlands at different periods. Since about the 11th century, dikes have been used to protect low-lying areas from the sea. One of the later types (bottom left) was made of wooden piles, but by the 17th century most of these had been destroyed by the shipworm. Polders were created by pumping out water from areas encircled by dikes— at first with windmills working in relays (right). Windmills are still occasionally used (above).

raised again. The plan proposed building a 25-mile dam to enclose the Zuider Zee, so reducing the length of coastline exposed to tides by as much as 200 miles. The dam, finished in 1932, provided the only long-term solution to the problems of the northern Netherlands. It is much easier to strengthen and raise the existing dam, if the sea continues to rise, than it is to reinforce and lengthen 200 miles of dikes along the former seashore. The dam is also invaluable in several other ways, as the Zuider Zee is now a fresh-water lake, known as the IJsselmeer, or Lake IJssel. Sluices in the dam keep back sea water at high tide. They open at low tide to let through fresh water from the IJssel River, at the same time flushing away salt water from the soil. The lake is now a vital fresh-water reserve for domestic and agricultural use during drought, and the former herring fishery has been replaced by fresh-water fishing. Moreover, there is no longer any threat of sea water intruding into the soil and canals, which previously ruined much of the agricultural land.

Large parts of Lake IJssel have been turned into polders. The first stage in the creation of a polder is to build an encircling dike, and to pump out the water. The old seabed is then drained by crisscrossing the land with ditches, which empty into a deeper ditch around the polder inside the dike. Reeds are often grown at this stage to help dry out the soil, to prevent weeds from taking root, and to stop the topsoil from blowing away. After a few years, underground drains are laid from which water empties into ditches, and is finally pumped up and out into Lake IJssel. Although most of the soil is basically fertile, it always needs careful treatment before it is ready for agriculture. Most of the land is used for arable farming, and the rest for dairy farming and market gardening.

Today, half the people of the Netherlands live below sea level, relying on dams, dikes, and sand dunes to protect themselves from inundation. But there is always a risk of flooding, and during the last 200 years each flood has been worse than the last (perhaps partly because the sea level all over the world is slowly rising). The conditions that lead to these disasters are complex, and are basically: (1) very low barometric pressure over the southern North Sea, which allows the sea level to rise; (2) spring tides; (3) northerly gales

in the North Sea together with a westerly gale in the English Channel. A combination of all these conditions is fortunately rare, but when a major flood does occur, immense damage is done to property as well as agricultural land. After the disastrous record flood of 1952, the Dutch wisely planned their new sea defenses with a long-term view on the assumption that future floods will be even higher.

The new defenses center around the deltas of the Rhine, Meuse, and Scheldt, in the southwest of the Netherlands, where the shoreline is about 600 miles long. Rather than go to the enormous expense of reinforcing or rebuilding existing defenses, the Dutch have conceived one of the world's great works of civil engineering, the Delta Project (see illustration). This consists of raising the seaward dikes of a number of islands and joining the islands by a series of dams, thus creating a complete barrier to the North Sea. The dams are being equipped with sluice gates up to 186 feet long. These gates open at low tide to release river water and winter ice, and close at high tide to exclude the sea from the branches of the estuary. What was formerly estuary will become fresh-water lakes, so that the problem of salt-water intrusion will be solved. Also, the sheltered water behind the dikes will be kept at a constant level and will help to satisfy a problem that is urgent in a heavily populated country like the Netherlands—that of providing opportunity for recreation, such as sailing, fishing, and water-skiing.

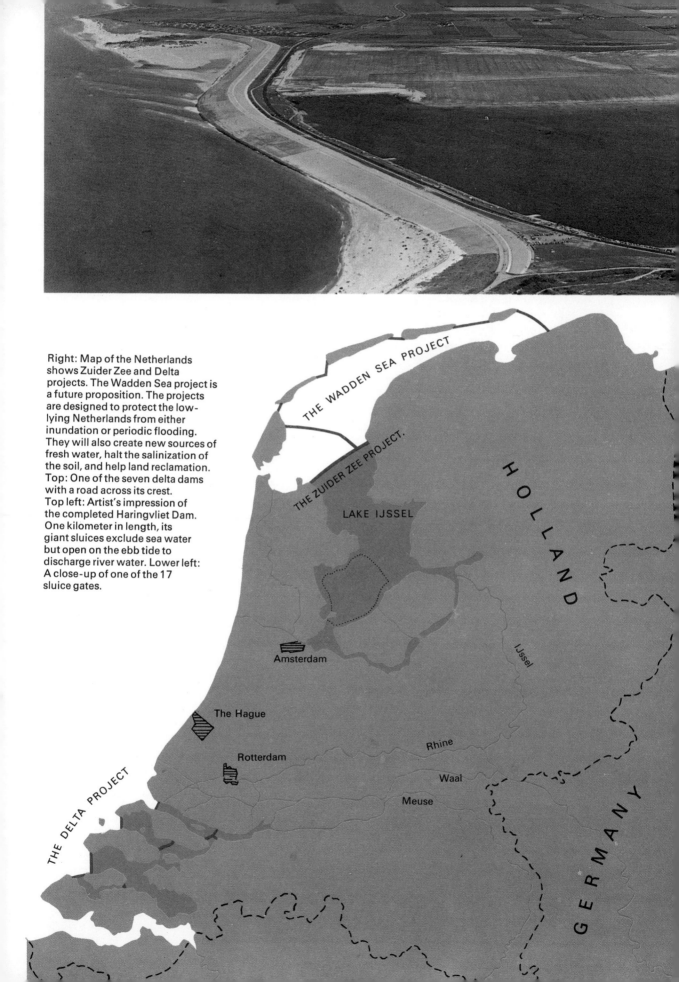

Right: Map of the Netherlands shows Zuider Zee and Delta projects. The Wadden Sea project is a future proposition. The projects are designed to protect the low-lying Netherlands from either inundation or periodic flooding. They will also create new sources of fresh water, halt the salinization of the soil, and help land reclamation.
Top: One of the seven delta dams with a road across its crest.
Top left: Artist's impression of the completed Haringvliet Dam. One kilometer in length, its giant sluices exclude sea water but open on the ebb tide to discharge river water. Lower left: A close-up of one of the 17 sluice gates.

THE WADDEN SEA PROJECT

THE ZUIDER ZEE PROJECT.

LAKE IJSSEL

HOLLAND

Amsterdam

The Hague

Rotterdam

IJssel

Rhine

Waal

Meuse

THE DELTA PROJECT

GERMANY

9 Irrigation and Agriculture

Irrigation means artificially watering the soil to initiate or increase the growth of crops. The first large irrigation projects developed in the Eastern Hemisphere about 4000 B.C. and made possible the advanced cultures of Egypt, Syria, Persia, India, Java, and Ceylon. In the Western Hemisphere, elaborate projects developed much later, about 2000 years ago, for example, in Mexico and Peru. Because the river flow or the amount and timing of the rainfall in these countries was inconsistent, success or failure often balanced on a razor edge. In fact, irrigation was the success it was only because social systems were largely concerned with making sure that it worked. This called for a high degree of personal discipline in the management of irrigation projects, and there were also strict rules that were enforced by inspectors. Careless irrigation ranked among the most serious of crimes, often punishable by death. In China, the prestige of some of the earlier kings was measured by their wisdom in using and controlling water.

Some ancient irrigation dams and canals are still in use and testify to the care and skill with which they were made. But they are only the remains of much larger projects that fell into ruin because it became impossible—especially in times of war—to keep up the constant vigilance and the enforcement of laws on which all successful irrigation depends. In general, the simple systems have lasted longest. During the last two centuries, as complex projects became necessary to supply rapidly growing populations with more food, the art of successful irrigation usually had to be rediscovered.

Irrigation accounts for most of the water used throughout the world. All agricultural land in Egypt is irrigated, about half in China, Japan, and Pakistan, about 33 million acres in the United States, and large parts of Europe. No country, in fact, is without its irrigation projects.

Yet only a small percentage of the agricultural land is irrigated—about 400 million acres—often using only a small proportion of the available water. One reason for this is that irrigation requires enormous quantities of water. For instance, one ton of sugar beets needs 1000 tons of water during its period of growth; wheat, 1500 tons and rice, 4000 tons. Furthermore, most of the water used for irrigation cannot be re-used. At least half of it is lost by evapotranspiration. The rest is incorporated into the plants themselves (which are over 60 per cent water), and drains down into the subsoil. At least it is possible to re-use a proportion of the water supplied to the domestic consumer and industry.

Many ancient methods of irrigation were as successful as those of the present day. An interesting example is that of *chinampa* farming, essential to the success of the Aztec empire. Chinampas were constructed on the edges of shallow lakes in the Valley of Mexico, and also extended into those lakes. They provided abundant food for civilians and soldiers, and were a successful attempt at land reclamation. An ancient Aztec map (top) shows that large areas were crisscrossed by canals, between which lay the chinampas, measuring about 300 by 30 feet. Earth excavated from the canals was dumped between them until the level was a few feet above the water. Waterweeds from the canals were placed on this earth—to form a natural compost heap—and on this was spread a thin layer of canal mud. The plots (below left) were kept in place by posts, and later by willow trees. Seeds were planted with human manure in a hole in small blocks of dried mud and vegetation (bottom right), and hand-watered; the seedlings were then transplanted to the chinampas. About seven different crops a year were obtained from each plot, including two of corn. The chinampas were periodically stripped and made up with new mud and vegetation from the canals so that there was no need for them to lie fallow.

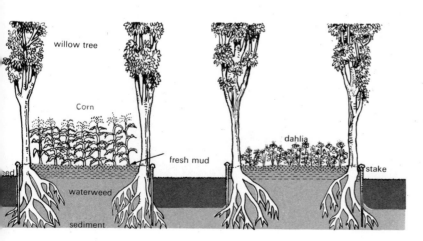

willow tree

Corn

dahlia

fresh mud

stake

waterweed

sediment

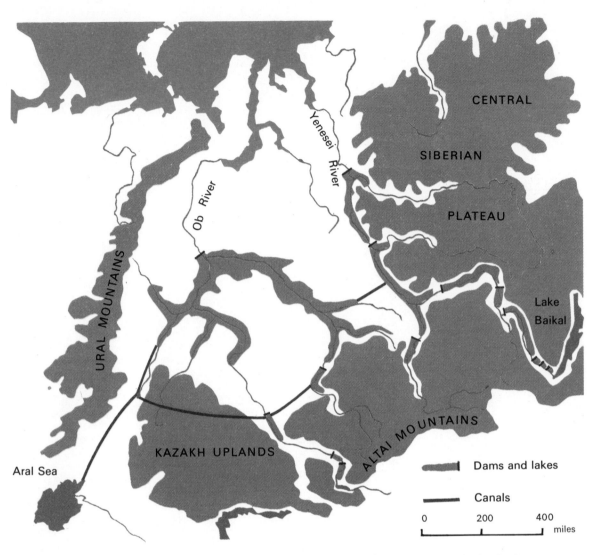

One U.S.S.R. project (above) involves diverting and storing river water that runs to waste in the Arctic Ocean in order to irrigate the central Soviet steppes. Below: An 18th-century engraving portrays the cultivation of rice in ancient China; in many parts of Asia the same techniques are still used. Of all crops, rice requires the most water. Even so, it remains the staple diet for over half of mankind.

This is not to say that we cannot further increase the acreage of irrigated land. Most countries have ambitious plans to do just this. For instance, Russia plans to build an immense dam on the Ob River, creating a lake nearly the size of Italy, into which water will pour by canal from the Yenisei River. From the Ob, water would flow through a vast system of canals, rivers, and lakes to the Aral Sea, irrigating on the way 50 million acres of cropland, and vast stretches of pasture in arid western Siberia. As for the underdeveloped countries, irrigation will presumably increase when there is better education and enough money to finance large works. Some regions, however, such as the Mekong River basin (Cambodia, Thailand, South Vietnam, Laos), will also have to wait for a more settled political situation.

By far the greatest area of irrigated land exists in hot, humid climates. Here the commonest crop is rice, which provides the main caloric intake for about one-third of the world's population. Most rice is grown in paddy fields that are flooded with about six inches of water during the growing season. There is usually no shortage of water in humid climates, either because the annual rainfall is very high, or because there are large rivers with a reliable flow. The problem is rather one of controlling and distributing large quantities of water at just the right time. If the rains come too early or too late, or if water is applied at the wrong time, rice suffers. Another problem in some humid areas is draining away the large surplus of water after the growing season.

In arid lands, on the other hand, the main problem of irrigating large areas is a shortage of water. It is most unlikely that there will ever be enough, which is unfortunate because the soil in arid zones can be very fertile. Even when countries have a local abundance of water, as in the north of Israel and the north of California, there is still not enough to irrigate the entire arid section. Agriculture in arid lands is also beset by problems that do not occur in humid regions. Sudden heavy storms, causing *flash floods*, are typical of these parts in the brief wet season. Where there is sloping land that is devoid of vegetation, water flows so quickly that it has no time to sink into the soil. On the other hand, on flat plains where there is bad drainage, irrigation may eventually raise the water table so that the land becomes waterlogged.

Good drainage is just as important as irrigation. In the past, many peoples have neglected this principle, and so millions of acres now lie unused. Waterlogging prevents oxygen from reaching plant roots, which then suffocate. Also, waterlogged soil does not encourage crops to develop deep roots, so that during drought they are unable to tap the deeper moist soil. Waterlogging occurs either because the water table reaches the surface or because water cannot seep down beyond the root zone. The latter situation can arise in three ways. First, the openings and channels in the topsoil may be too small for water to infiltrate quickly enough; this can be avoided by proper cultivation of the topsoil (p. 126). Second, the subsoil may be too compact to let water through; this is remedied by deep plowing. Third, the subsoil may be naturally impermeable, as when it consists of clay; in this case, the only solution is to lay underground drains that discharge surplus water into specially dug ditches.

One very serious effect of waterlogging in arid

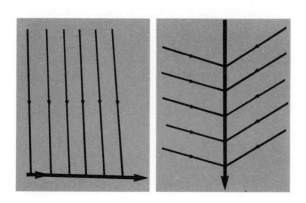

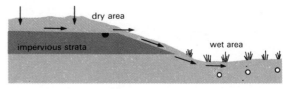

Efficient agriculture in areas with poor natural drainage depends as much on artificial drainage as on irrigation. The diagram above indicates how a wet area might arise. The diagrams at left suggest two possible layouts for the drains.

regions is the accumulation of natural salts in the soil, called *salinization*. High salt concentrations affect plants in two ways. Certain salts, such as boron, are toxic in excess. And when the *total* concentration of various salts is too high, water is unable to enter plant roots, and may even leave them to enter the soil. In hot, dry weather, evaporation is extremely fast from the soil surface, and since all irrigation water contains salts (except for stored rainwater), these are left behind in the soil. Say, for example, river water used for irrigation contains 400 parts of salt per million parts of water. Then if 12 inches evaporates from one acre (*an acre-foot*), about a half ton of salt per acre would be left behind. But it is difficult to avoid salinization in arid regions. If too much water is used, the level of high water tables rises until water reaches the surface by capillary action and then evaporates, leaving behind salts in the topsoil. If, on the other hand, too little water is used, accumulated salts are not flushed to below the root zone.

The right quantity of water to use depends on the concentration of its salts, the permeability of the soil, the level of the water table, and the type of crop. Poor quality water can be used for permeable soils with deep water tables; better quality water must be used for less permeable soils. Furthermore, crops differ in their tolerance to salts, and also require different quantities of water. And lastly, it is important to apply water at just the right time, and this too varies from one crop to another. Really efficient irrigation is thus not simply a matter of applying water to the soil and waiting for crops to flourish. It requires a knowledge of soil-water conditions in relation to the particular crop to be grown.

Waterlogging and salinization exist in many parts of the world, especially in arid regions. They are particularly serious in countries that rely on their own land to provide food for a large population, rather than on heavy imports. West Pakistan, for example, with a population of 43 million (1964), is the largest single irrigated region in the world. Out of 39 million acres of fertile soil, 23 million are irrigated by an exten-

Salinization of the soil is a serious problem in many parts of the world because it is extremely expensive to flush the salts into the subsoil. The aerial photograph above shows waterlogged fields (black), salt patches (white), and unaffected fields (gray). One of the worst-afflicted regions is West Pakistan (right), of which a typical waterlogged area is shown on the far right.

sive system of boreholes and feeder canals. Yet the population lives in hunger and poverty, because even the vast, fertile Indus plain cannot provide enough food, due to inefficient irrigation and farming practices. The flat plain of West Pakistan has very poor natural drainage, and irrigation has produced 11 million acres of waterlogged land. The main cause of this is that a third of the water in irrigation canals has seeped through their beds and has raised the water table. Waterlogging, coupled with the high rate of evaporation, has, in turn, ruined 5 million acres by salinization. In other parts, salinization has been caused by farmers using too little irrigation water during the dry season.

West Pakistan is at present engaged in one of the largest engineering projects in the world, in an attempt to reclaim these lost acres and to increase the quantity of water available for irrigation. Thousands of boreholes are being sunk to transfer ground water to the canals and thus lower the water table. The extra water in the canals is then used to flush accumulated salts from the topsoil. At the same time, efforts are being made to increase the crop yield by using fertilizers and better seed strains. The pattern of the new irrigation projects is largely a result of the Indus Water Treaty of 1960, which settled a long dispute with India. The treaty states that by 1970 the three eastern tributaries will be used by India alone. Pakistan is therefore diverting the three western tributaries into canals at present dependent on those in the east. This is being achieved by a system of canals, barrages, and dams, including two immense earth dams, Mangla and Tarbela, that will conserve some of the floodwater of the Indus. However, surface storage is not a final solution. The Mangla and Tarbela reservoirs may be silted up in about 50 years and there are few sites for new reservoirs. Greater use will then have to be made of the extensive aquifer in the north, which is already tapped by half a million wells. With its enormous capacity, this aquifer would be better able to store floodwater than are surface reservoirs.

With the help of foreign aid and knowledge, at

least the old mistakes of waterlogging and salinization are not being repeated. Where possible, the beds of new canals lie below the water table so that they act as large drains (rather like an effluent river, p. 68), as well as serving for irrigation. Canals with beds above the water table are sealed to prevent water leaking out and raising the water table. But the most difficult task is persuading farmers to adopt modern methods. This involves abandoning many ancient social customs, as well as introducing a new system of land tenure that gives some incentive to improve the land.

There are several methods of irrigation. The most effective for a particular area depends on the hilliness of the land, the nature of the soil, the type of crop, and the amount of available money. One of the oldest systems is *basin flooding*, and was the sole method used in the flat Nile valley until the middle of the nineteenth century. Land near the river is divided into lots ranging from 1 to 40 thousand acres, surrounded by artificial banks. When the Nile rises in summer, water enters the basins through short canals and sluices, flooding the land to a depth of three to six feet. The water remains in the basins from 40 to 60 days, and deposits a fine layer of silt. When the river falls, water drains out of the basins, leaving behind moist land of renewed fertility. This system is simple and effective, except when the river level is abnormally low or high. It is the only type of irrigation that automatically fertilizes the land. But with a growing population, Egypt has been forced to develop elaborate systems to irrigate fields not reached by the annual flood.

The transfer of water from a river through *canals* has been used since Babylonian times. It is still one of the commonest ways of bringing water to crops. If the river has a steep gradient, water is diverted into a canal some distance upstream, and led along a contour so that it can flow to fields by gravity. If the river has only a slight gradient, like the Nile, low dams with sluices, called *barrages*, are built at intervals to raise the river level. From each barrage, water flows by canal to land that lies above the natural river level but below the raised level of the barrage. Canals are expensive to build, especially if watertight. They also need occasional dredging to free them from deposited silt.

Egyptians have grown crops for thousands of years with the aid of water and fertile silt from the Nile. The old system of basin irrigation relied on the summer flooding of the river. Seed was sown in autumn, restricting the crops to those that could survive the cooler winter—wheat, barley, clover. Today, an improved system of irrigation supplies water all the year round, and corn and cotton are also grown. With continuous irrigation, a dam holds back part of the high river flow, which passes during the dry season into canals along edge of valley (below). Water drains through sluices in canals back to Nile via ditches in fields. The chart on the right shows a year's farming on the lower Nile.

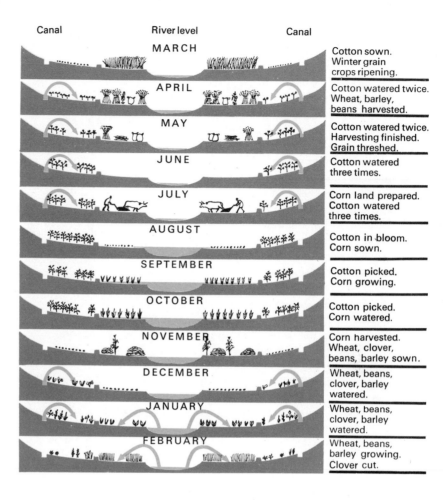

Canal	River level	Canal	
	MARCH		Cotton sown. Winter grain crops ripening.
	APRIL		Cotton watered twice. Wheat, barley, beans harvested.
	MAY		Cotton watered twice. Harvesting finished. Grain threshed.
	JUNE		Cotton watered three times.
	JULY		Corn land prepared. Cotton watered three times.
	AUGUST		Cotton in bloom. Corn sown.
	SEPTEMBER		Cotton picked. Corn growing.
	OCTOBER		Cotton picked. Corn watered.
	NOVEMBER		Corn harvested. Wheat, clover, beans, barley sown.
	DECEMBER		Wheat, beans, clover, barley watered.
	JANUARY		Wheat, beans, clover, barley watered.
	FEBRUARY		Wheat, beans, barley growing. Clover cut.

Right: The Sennar Dam across the Blue Nile diverts water into two irrigation canals in the Gezira cotton plantations, Sudan. Left: The Gezira plantations neatly divided into plots by irrigation canals and furrows.

113

This can be reduced by constructing sedimentation pools near the canal intake. Waterweeds also are a menace.

Another method of irrigation used since ancient times involves lifting water from *wells* into channels that cross a field. Wells are the only source of water in many arid regions, but are seldom used to irrigate large areas. In poor arid areas many ingenious devices to lift water are still used, such as the shadoof (a counterbalanced bucket), the Archimedean screw lift, the windlass, waterwheels, and others. Gradually, though, these methods are being replaced by power-driven pumps. But with these, great care has to be taken that the ground water is not permanently depleted.

An interesting method of collecting water to irrigate arid regions is the *kanat*. This consists of a tunnel that collects underground water from an aquifer at the foot of a mountain. Water flows along the gently sloping tunnel to the irrigated region by gravity, maybe for 30 miles. Every so often, vertical shafts extend from the tunnel to the surface, and give workmen access for repairs and for removing earth. Several thousand miles of kanats exist from North Africa to Asia, and are still used, the most famous being the vast network in Iran (Persia).

The most recent method of irrigation involves overhead *sprinklers*, from which water falls like rain. Sprinklers consist either of perforated pipes through which water flows under pressure, or of a rotating nozzle at the end of a pressure pipe that flings water over a large area. The great advantage of sprinklers is their lightness; they can be carried to different parts of a field as needed. They are also the only economic means of irrigating hilly terrain. Water from sprinklers is easily and accurately applied, and the method is especially useful where labor is short.

Perforated pipes can also be laid beneath the surface of the soil—a method called *subsurface irrigation*. With sprinklers, about 10 per cent of the water evaporates before reaching the ground and about 20 per cent from the soil. Such losses do not occur with careful subsurface irrigation, which is invaluable in arid regions. Unfortunately, there are few soils where this method is practical, because the openings in the pipes become blocked. Gravel or sandy soil is the best for this purpose.

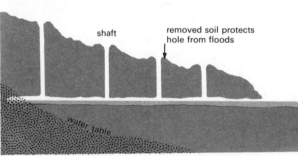

shaft

removed soil protects hole from floods

water table

Kanats (above) have been used for over 3000 years, and many thousands of miles of them still convey irrigation water. A kanat consists of a gently sloping tunnel leading from an aquifer to the irrigation area. Earth is removed through vertical shafts during excavation and repairs. Shafts also provide access for food and air for the workmen. Top: Photograph shows men repairing a kanat.

Top right: A field of soybeans is irrigated by pumping water from a ditch through sprinklers. These are moved about so that the whole field is well watered. Bottom right: Water gushes from an artesian borehole in the desert of southern Jordan and provides water for irrigation.

So far we have dealt with methods of irrigating existing soils. But all that plants require from soil is anchorage, and a supply of water, oxygen, and inorganic salts. This leads to an interesting method of cultivation in which soil is made artificially with small stones, or even plastic pellets, to provide anchorage. Nutrients are supplied in the irrigation water. This method of cultivation, called *hydroponics*, is particularly useful in isolated, barren places where vegetables cannot be grown, such as the Cape Verde Islands in the Atlantic. It is also being increasingly used in growing intensive crops under glass in Europe and America.

A typical hydroponics plot consists of a level enclosure with waterproof sides and bottom. Seeds are sown in the gravel, and then the nutrient solution is pumped into the enclosure at regular intervals so as to flood the gravel without wetting the surface. After each flooding, the solution drains away and is used again and again. As the solution drains away, air is drawn into the interstices between the gravel to provide roots with oxygen.

Hydroponics has several advantages, such as high yields, less root disease, and less requirement for labor. The concentration of nutrients can be exactly controlled, and there is better aeration than with normal soils. Also, since the surface of the bed remains dry, there is less loss by evaporation than there is with conventional irrigation of fields. For instance, hydroponically grown tomatoes require half as much irrigation water as do tomatoes grown conventionally. Experiments in the Negev desert in Israel have also shown that it is possible to use water with a high concentration of dissolved salts—water that cannot be used for irrigation by any other method. In this process, certain compounds are added in exact amounts to the irrigation

Right: A hydroponic bed under construction. Sections of pipe are laid with gaps between them, and covered with sand. Every second day, water with nutrients is pumped through pipes until sand is saturated. The solution is then allowed to drain out of the sloping beds at one end, and stored for re-use. As the water drains out, air is sucked in. Thus plants receive an almost ideal combination of air, water, and nutrients.

After two years of intensive, continuous cultivation, disease begins to affect plants. The sand is then sterilized (right) by covering it with plastic and saturating with steam.

Right: Commercial flower-growing under glass and by using hydroponic beds is very successful.

Left: Hydroponic beds being used in the open in Israel. Water with nutrients is pumped from tanks in foreground.

The Israeli wadi above is surrounded by bare countryside that is scoured into weird shapes as a result of flash floods. These occur only a few times in a year but are very violent. The ancient peoples of the Negev used to collect rain flowing over hard-baked earth in channels and divert it to make lush irrigated plots in the valleys. This system of runoff farming is now being redeveloped (left).

Right: Dusting an Australian lake with cetyl alcohol. This forms a very thin protective film and gives the lake a mirror-smooth surface. In calm weather, the film reduces evaporation by as much as 50 per cent at a cost of about 1 cent per 1000 gallons saved. With winds of moderate strength, however, the film breaks and may pile up on the shore.

water to "neutralize" the salts' harmful effects.

These, then, are the methods of irrigation, all of which require a large source of water. But if there are no large rivers or lakes within a reasonable distance, water must be stored during the wet season. This is not as easy as it sounds. What we call "arid regions" do have a short wet season. But when the rain comes, it is usually torrential and very sudden, producing flash floods that are difficult and costly to collect. And to make matters worse, there are excessive losses by evaporation from stored water in arid climates. A great deal of thought has been given to ways of reducing evaporation, but the only remedy so far has been to apply a small quantity of an organic substance, such as cetyl alcohol, on the surface of a reservoir. In calm weather, this spreads out into a film only one molecule thick and reduces evaporation. This has been tried with some success in Australia, but with moderate winds the film breaks just when evaporation is fastest.

An alternative way of reducing evaporation is to build deeper reservoirs so as to reduce the ratio of surface to volume. But these are costly to build, and it is interesting to know that Australia has a project to create a large, deep reservoir below the land surface in a matter of seconds by exploding an atomic device.

In recent years, there have been some attempts to transport water from far-away lakes and reservoirs. Only well-developed countries, however, have been able to overcome the cost and difficulty of such a task because, as we have seen, effective irrigation requires enormous quantities of water. One land that is being transformed in this way is Israel. The ancient Israelites had no large river to provide water for irrigation, unlike the more fortunate Mesopotamians and Egyptians. Agriculture depended entirely on direct rainfall, which varied from about 40 inches a year in the north to only 1 inch a year in the southern part of the Negev desert. Early settlers in the Negev, however, developed ingenious methods for irrigating small patches of land, such as by trapping dew or sinking wells in wadi beds. They also developed a system of diverting rain that flowed over the hard-baked soil into channels and hollows. Some of these ancient systems still work effectively.

The prophet Ezekiel's vision told of a "land traversed by a great river, fringed with many trees, whose waters go down into the desert and where everything shall live whither the river cometh." Centuries later this dream began to be realized. At the Paris Peace Conference in 1919, it was agreed to include Lake Tiberias and part of the Jordan River within the borders of Palestine so that irrigation might be possible. After the State of Israel was formed in 1948, it was decided to concentrate on the driest part, the Negev, where irrigation would yield the most benefit. Much of this desert is potentially very fertile, and flat enough for mechanized cultivation, pipe-laying, and road-building. Since it has a healthy climate and small population, its development would relieve congestion in other parts of Israel.

During the summer, only a little dew moistens the land. Rain falls only in the four winter months and is quite variable. Much of the rain rushes in sudden torrents into streams and wadis and hence into the Mediterranean and the Jordan River. Attempts to trap these sudden rainfalls in reservoirs have proved unsuccessful. The only solution was to transport large quantities of water from Lake Tiberias 150 miles away. The immense 108-inch-diameter concrete pipeline leading from the lake now also links up previous projects into one integrated system (see illustration p. 120).

By 1970, the population of Israel will have reached about three million and Lake Tiberias cannot supply all the extra water needed. Experiments are therefore in progress to intercept flash floods and recharge the water underground —a very difficult task. In addition, more wells will be dug, and efforts are to be made to purify municipal sewage. A desalination plant is also to be built at Tel Aviv.

Right: A map of Israel's main water projects. The largest scheme—the National Water Carrier—involves pumping about 84 billion gallons annually 1200 feet up from Lake Tiberias (Sea of Galilee) into an aqueduct. In this it flows by gravity 84 miles to Rosh Ha'ayin, and from there it flows to the Negev. The Western Galilee-Kishon project uses water from wells, springs, rivers, and reclaimed sewage in Galilee's western foothills for irrigation and municipal supplies. The Lake Tiberias-Beit She'an project, which supplies the Jordan and Beit She'an valleys, was begun after Jordan diverted the Yarmuk River for its own use. The Yarkon-Negev project carries water from wells and the Yarkon River to the Negev. The Elath supply project supplies well-water to the rapidly growing port of Elath. Only adequate finances and a tremendous national ambition make these projects possible in such an arid country.

▲ pumping stations

═══ canals

● reservoirs

••••• tunnel

━━━ pipeline

----- boundaries

━━━ other major water projects

1 National Water Carrier
2 Western Galilee—Kishon project
3 Lake Tiberias—Beit She'an project
4 Yarkon—Negev project
5 Elath supply project

Top left: Channels at Beit She'an, Israel, mix water from different springs to obtain a tolerable dilution of salts. Top right: The production of 108-inch-diameter prestressed concrete waterpipes. Sections of these (below) are used to carry water part of the way from Lake Tiberias to the Negev.

Large storage reservoirs for irrigation are usually economical only when they also serve another purpose. One such plan is the Snowy Mountains project in Australia, which has been called one of the "seven future engineering wonders of the world." It is partly a hydro-electric project, and the total cost of the project will be repaid by the sale of electricity. Australia is largely desert with a rainfall of less than 10 inches a year, and has one of the highest evaporation rates in the world. The small population of 12 million (1964) lives mostly in the well-watered strip along the east and southeast coasts, and along the northern edge. Much of the crop production depends on irrigation, but this must increase to support a rapidly expanding population.

The Snowy Mountains—the highest land in Australia—are snowbound for five months of the year, and give rise to three large rivers: the Murray and the Murrumbidgee, which flow westward across dry and fertile plains, and the Snowy, which flows southward through the well-watered coastal belt. The Snowy Mountains project (see illustration opposite) is designed to increase the irrigated land along the Murray and Murrumbidgee rivers by storing the surplus snow-melt in large reservoirs, which will then augment the flow of the two rivers during the dry summer. It also involves diverting the Snowy River, via tunnels and reservoirs, to the Murray and Murrumbidgee. The project, due for completion in 1970, covers 2500 square miles, and involves 17 large dams, 9 power stations, and 80 miles of aqueducts high in the ranges to collect mountain streams that would otherwise miss the reservoirs. Water from various rivers passes to the reservoirs through 100 miles of tunnels.

Irrigation projects that enable enough crops to be grown to feed a large part of the population—as in Israel and Australia—are possible only because four conditions prevail: The population is relatively small; there is a large quantity of water that can be transported from at least one part of the country; there is sufficient money to build long-term, multipurpose projects; and farmers are well enough educated to accept the techniques of modern agriculture. Where one or more of these conditions is absent, much can still be done to improve agriculture in arid regions by making the best use of what water there is, and by properly cultivating the soil. In parts of Tunisia, for example, where there is not enough ground or surface water, a million acres of fruit-trees have been planted on soil that catches and holds the nighttime dew.

This map of southern Australia shows irrigated land (gray) along the Murray and Murrumbidgee rivers. Both rivers arise in the Snowy Mountains. The Snowy Mountains project aims to increase the river flows in summer by storing surplus spring runoff in reservoirs connected to the rivers by tunnels.

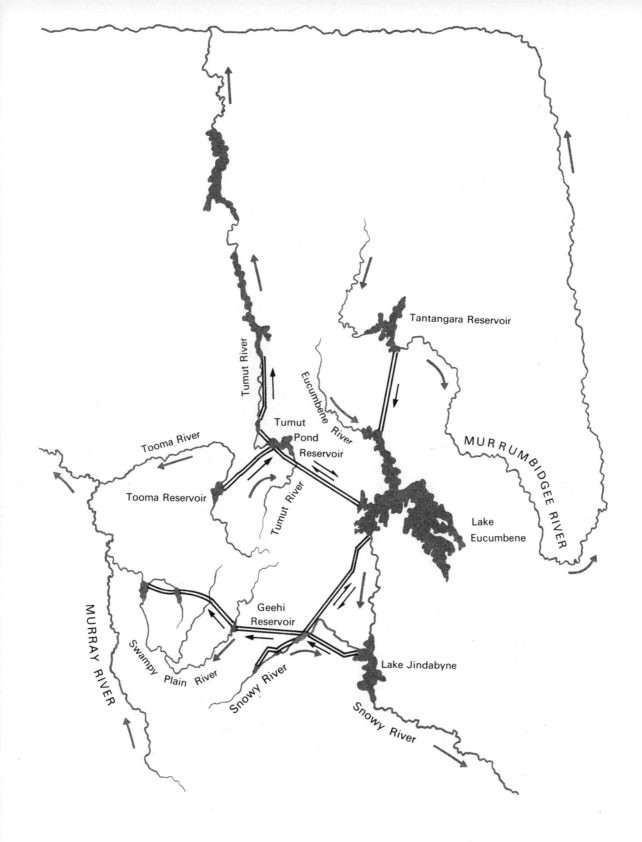

The above map shows the catchment area of the Snowy Mountains project. Blue arrows denote direction of river flow, black arrows the direction of flow through tunnels (black lines). The *Snowy-Tumut project:* As the snow melts in spring, surplus water from the Eucumbene, Upper Murrumbidgee, and Tooma rivers passes to Lake Eucumbene, mostly through tunnels. When river levels fall, the stored water enters a two-way tunnel that leads to the Tumut River, which in turn feeds the Murrumbidgee River. The *Snowy-Murray project:* In spring, surplus water from the Snowy River passes to Lake Eucumbene through a two-way tunnel; in summer, water passes back through same tunnel, and then to the Swampy Plain River—a tributary of the Murray. Water will also be pumped from Lake Jindabyne into this tunnel, and during off-peak hours will rise 750 feet up to the Geehi Reservoir. From here water will fall 2600 feet to the Murray River, generating large quantities of hydroelectric power.

Top left: A surveyor in Australia's Snowy Mountains; note the rugged terrain and great height at which part of the Snowy Mountains project is being carried out. Before work began, roads had to be built and then kept clear of deep snow (top right) during winter. The main storage reservoir in the project is Lake Eucumbene (middle left); water flows to and from it along giant tunnels (middle right). At various points, hydroelectric stations (above) extract power as water falls thousands of feet.

Recently, there has been renewed interest in the effects of dew and fog on vegetation. (Fog consists of droplets of water in the air; dew forms when water vapor condenses on a cool surface.) In some parts of the world, dew or fog is the sole source of water for plants, as along the rainless coast of Peru. Fog is responsible for the distribution of plants along the west-central coast of North America. Along the south coast of Hokkaido in Japan, special strips of forest are planted to catch the fog moving inland. When there is a large amount of moisture, drops of water condense on leaves, fall to the ground, and are then absorbed by plant roots. With certain plants, condensed moisture is absorbed directly by the leaves, although how common or important this is no one knows.

Where agriculture is concerned, great advances in utilizing dew have been made by the Israelis in the Negev. Here the total annual rainfall varies from one to eight inches, all of which may fall within 10 days. The amount of dew, on the other hand, is very great, especially in the driest and hottest part of the country. Measurements showed that some dew occurs during 250 nights of the year and heavy dew on 140 of them.

Some authorities claim that the Israelites collected dew thousands of years ago with mounds of stones. When these cooled at night by radiation, water vapor condensed on their surfaces and then ran down to water the base of a vine plant. Be that as it may, today the Israelites use sloping plastic sheets with a gutter at the bottom edge. Dew runs down the sheet into the gutter, and from here gravitates along a duct to a pit around each seedling. The .96 gallons that collect each month on about 10 square feet of sheet is enough to keep seedlings alive until the winter rains. The same device, of course, can be used to collect rain. A sheet 10 feet square in area supplying a pit 1 foot square provides 10 times as much water as when rain falls directly on the pit.

As a result of dew collecting, there now stand in the Negev desert avenues and woods of eucalyptus, Aleppo pine, and other trees. The method is simple, and avoids the cost of irrigation canals and pipelines. And because dew is almost pure distilled water, it is effective in flushing out accumulated salts from the soil. There is no reason why dew collecting should not be effective in some other deserts of the world, such as in Peru and Chile, which have a yearly 1½

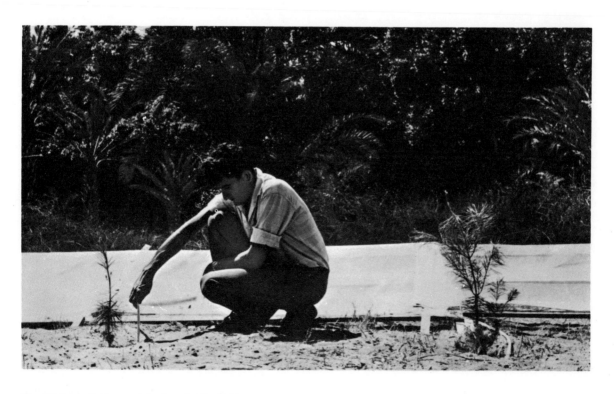

The photograph shows a sloping plastic sheet used for dew-trapping in Israel. Dew flows into a gutter at base of sheet, and then down a pipe to a pit at base of seedling. Enough dew forms to keep seedlings alive until the arrival of the rains.

125

inches of rain but as much as 16 inches of dew.

Agriculture in areas where there is little rainfall and no possibility of irrigation is called *dry farming*. It is especially effective for crops like barley, wheat, and sorghums. Although widely practiced, really efficient dry farming is not easy, and many countries have learned the art only during the last 50 years. The first condition for dry farming is to plant crops that are drought resistant and whose main growth period lies in the wet season. Just as important is to remove weeds and unnecessary plant growth, otherwise the little water present may be soon lost by transpiration. Furthermore, there is often too little water to cope with the continuous transpiration of the crop alone. In such a case, the land is plowed and left fallow for a year or two so as to allow it to build up a store of water.

Another technique used in dry farming is to prepare a *tilth*, which is a surface layer of small, loose, soil crumbs. The large openings and channels in such a layer permit rain to seep immediately into the soil. This is in contrast to hard-baked surfaces, over which water flows away or stands as puddles until it evaporates. To a certain extent, tilth also reduces evaporation from the underlying moist layer. Evaporation from the surface of damp soil is proportional to the wind speed and heat energy falling onto it. Evaporation continues as long as water at the surface is replenished by the upward movement of water by capillarity. Tilth reduces evaporation because the small capillary tubes are broken, and it protects the soil below from the sun and wind.

The main difficulty with dry farming is to prevent the correct tilth structure from being destroyed too quickly by wind and rain. If the crumbs are too fine, they are blown away. If the land is not flat, muddy water flows over the surface and blocks the openings with sediment. Driving rain also blocks soil openings by knocking particles into them. The commonest way of preserving the correct tilth structure is by contour plowing, in which the furrows follow the contour of the land and trap rain. Another method sometimes used is *mulching*—that is, covering the soil with dead plant matter. This breaks the impact of rain, which reaches the soil as a slow trickle without plugging the pores. Mulch also prevents the sun and wind from drying out the soil surface. Many successful experiments are also being done with plastic

mulching, whereby the soil is first irrigated and then covered with plastic sheets.

Irrigation is usually of no use unless the soil is well looked after. Proper cultivation of the soil, however, takes so much time and skill that it is not surprising that vast tracts of land now lie barren. But most countries are gradually learning from past mistakes. The dangers of waterlogging and salinization are now appreciated; drainage is considered as important as irrigation. The greatest difficulty in improving agriculture at present is undoubtedly educating and persuading farmers in developing countries to adopt modern methods, such as using the correct amount of water, fertilizers, and better seed strains. Primitive methods of farming have developed along with rigid social and religious customs, while in parts of the East, politics are also involved. All this will doubtless change, but persuasion is difficult when farmers can neither read nor write. One also meets a lack of interest, due to disease and malnutrition, and the conviction that famine will result if the new suggested methods fail. We can see, therefore, that there is a lot more to successful, world-wide irrigation than just providing enough water.

Opposite page: Clear plastic mulch being laid in a field of strawberries; the plants are brought through holes in the sheets. Plastic mulch raises the soil temperature, and increases yields by over 70 per cent. Below: A close-up view of plastic mulching. This modern technique can also be very useful in suppressing evaporation from the soil.

Right: 5000 Tanzanians pray for rain in the open fields. A drought in 1965 meant the closure of many farms and the prospect of starvation.

10　Pollution and Treatment

The greatest advance in water supplies has been made in the last 50 years, when water became available that was free from disease-producing organisms. This, as we have said before, is far more important than providing water in large quantities or free from taste. But in many parts of the world, we also expect water to be palatable, or pleasant to drink. This means that water must be reasonably oxygenated, and free from tastes and odors produced by algae, fungi, industrial waste, or sewage. It should not have any color, which apart from being unsightly, stains fabrics and appliances. Finally, we prefer water that is not too soft, which corrodes pipes and containers, and not too hard, which wastes soap, produces scum, and furs hot water pipes and cooking vessels. This chapter describes how we obtain such so-called *pure* water.

We have to be careful about the use of the word "pure" because pure water, consisting solely of H_2O molecules, does not exist. It cannot even be prepared in the laboratory. So when we talk about purifying water we really mean making it safe and palatable. The purest natural water comes from dew and rain in areas free from industrial, air-borne pollution. In industrial regions, as housewives know only too well, rain can quickly mark clothes on the line with dark streaks. All rain, however, collects small amounts of gases and dust as it descends through the air.

Ground water is often very clear, and because it has slowly filtered through the ground, it is generally free from silt, organic compounds, and microorganisms. But as water travels through the ground it dissolves part of the soil and rock, and so is usually hard. It may even contain objectionable concentrations of salts, such as those of iron and manganese. Surface waters (rivers, lakes, and reservoirs) contain the most

pollutants, for as water flows over the land it picks up silt, inorganic salts, and organic compounds from decayed plants and animals. Surface water, unlike ground water, also invariably contains microorganisms.

Really severe pollution, especially by harmful microorganisms, started only when rapidly growing populations in the Industrial Revolution began to discharge untreated sewage (called *raw sewage*) into rivers and lakes. Human waste was formerly carted off and spread on the land, where it was naturally decomposed by soil organisms. This, however, became impracticable for large towns and there was really no choice but to use rivers to remove waste. In some parts of the world, including parts of America and Europe, raw sewage is still discharged into rivers, so that many are now no more than open sewers. With the Industrial Revolution, however, came a new source of pollution in the form of effluents from industry. Today industry is responsible for more than twice as much pollution as is domestic sewage. A single sugar-beet factory, for example, produces pollutants equivalent to the sewage of a city of half a million. The food, textile, paper, and petroleum industries are other prime offenders. Some industrial effluents are actually more serious than household waste, for as well as containing organic material, they may include inorganic compounds like sulfuric acid, arsenic, and cyanides, which are difficult to remove and highly poisonous.

With thousands of tons of municipal and industrial waste being produced each year, it is inevitable that ground water should occasionally become polluted. This is most likely to happen in populated chalk and limestone areas where there are large fissures through which water travels so quickly that there is insufficient time for the

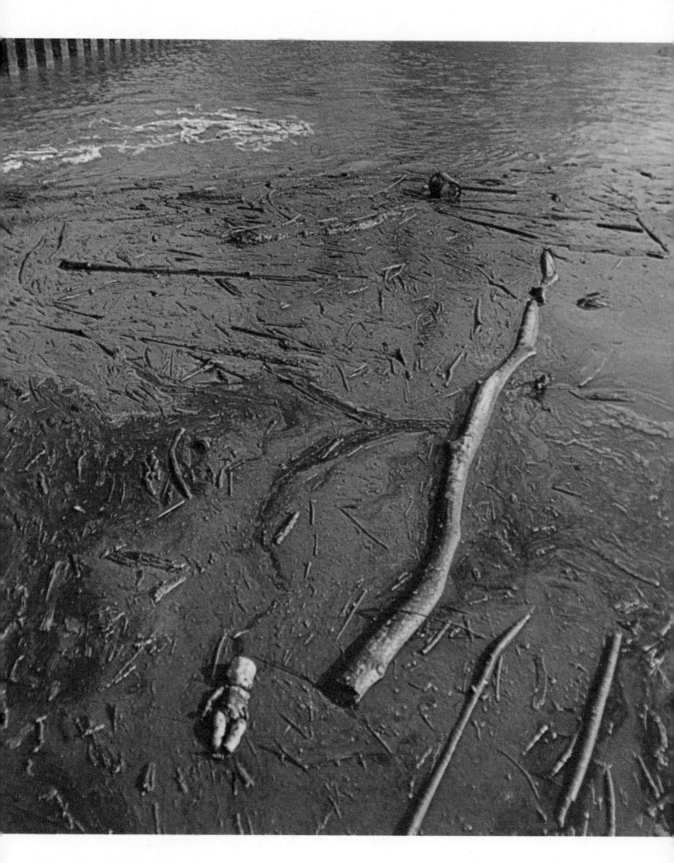

This river is laden with domestic and industrial
waste, and is just one of many polluted streams
pouring into Lake Erie. Enormous sums are being
spent to rescue the lake for the considerable
population and industry that depends on it.

129

natural process of purification. In such areas, a fractured sewer, for instance, may quickly infect wells with pathogenic organisms. In general, most organic compounds and microorganisms are destroyed before they reach wells, but this is not so for industrial effluents that contain substances that cannot be broken down by microorganisms. Detergents, for example, often enter wells in rural areas where household waste is disposed of in cesspools or by spreading on land that overlies aquifers.

A polluted aquifer is in many ways more of a problem than a polluted river or lake. It is very difficult or impossible to remedy, and an abandoned well is like money thrown away. However, it is not always possible to avoid the contamination of aquifers, or to foresee whether a borehole is likely to penetrate an already contaminated aquifer. There is the case of a firm in Norwich, England, that drilled a 36-inch-diameter borehole and later had to abandon it because tarlike substances and phenols suddenly appeared in the water. The pollutants appeared to have come from a gasworks, which was puzzling because the nearest one was some distance away. Eventually it was discovered that a gasworks built in 1815 had formerly occupied the actual site of the borehole and this had produced gas from the distillation of whale-oil. The tar had persisted in the ground for over 120 years!

The almost total lack of pollution control during the past century has resulted in rivers and lakes throughout the world that are polluted and almost useless for water supplies. Until recently, the attitude has often been to dump waste into a river and to leave it to be dealt with by the next consumer downstream. Sometimes legal action by downstream consumers forced people upstream to mend their ways, while occasionally all the river-users cooperated to prevent pollution. Such cooperation, however, was not possible for rivers and lakes bordered by several states or countries with different laws and degrees of "pollution consciousness." For example, Lake Erie, one of the Great Lakes, is bordered by five states and Canada and by 1965 was seriously polluted. Profuse algal growths thrived on the nutrients from untreated city sewage, while numerous cities along its edge dumped raw acid, oil, iron, car tires, and other rubbish into its shallow waters. Detroit alone poured in about 750 tons of waste each day. The fishing industry was destroyed, and at least $100 million are now needed to clean up the lake and prevent it from becoming an offensive swamp.

Probably the most polluted large river in the world is the Rhine, which, with its tributaries, passes through Switzerland, Liechtenstein, Austria, Germany, France, Luxembourg, Belgium, and Holland. Numerous industries in several of these countries have dumped waste, regardless of the next country downstream. A large amount of untreated sewage also entered the river from the 40 million inhabitants of the Rhine river basin. West Germany, for example, poured 73 per cent of its sewage into the Rhine and its tributaries, of which only 11 per cent was fully treated. Sometimes there were high levels of sodium chloride in the river from untreated sewage and industrial effluents, which, as we know, cannot

Far left: An open drain carries sewage alongside a street in Calcutta, India. Such drains endanger health by contaminating water supplies and ponds where people wash kitchen utensils, clothes, and themselves. Left: The drained Grand Surrey Canal, England, is visible proof that people regard waterways as convenient rubbish dumps. Right: Heaps of detergent foam on the Trent River, England. This sort of pollution can be reduced by persuading industry to make "soft" detergents, which microorganisms can decompose.

be removed economically. High concentrations of detergents were also common, and caused tastes and foaming of drinking water. In 1960, 10 per cent of the population of Essen had non-bacterial gastroenteritis, which was attributed to the irritant effect of the high salt and detergent concentrations.

Pollution is now so serious that several countries have enforced the treatment of all wastes. Agreements are also being gradually drawn up to prevent excessive pollution of international lakes and rivers, like Lake Erie and the Rhine. For the small firm, the cost of treating its effluents may be prohibitive, but this is still no excuse for polluting water used by other consumers. Under pressure, most firms incorporate effluent treatment in their budget without too much trouble. Fortunately, it is not too late to clean up our polluted lakes and rivers. For example, around Lake Michigan is the largest concentration of steel industries and oil refineries in the world. They have been forced to treat their effluents, and the lake is slowly recovering. This shows that pollution is not an inevitable outcome of large populations and heavy industry.

In practice, it is not necessary to remove all impurities from water before discharge into rivers and lakes. Such a course would be very expensive, especially as a city of 500,000 produces about 112 tons of solid sewage each day. Nature has kindly made water self-purifying to a large extent. Suspended solids settle out, particularly in lakes and reservoirs. Inorganic substances, such as iron, are oxidized by the dissolved oxygen in the water. Organic compounds

from sewage and industry are also oxidized into harmless carbon dioxide, water, sulfates, phosphates, and nitrates. This natural conversion is done by bacteria and other microorganisms, which find in sewage a rich source of food and energy. During breakdown, oxygen is gradually removed from the water, and is replenished by absorption from the air at the surface. If too much waste is present, oxygen is removed faster than it can be replenished. Decomposition is then taken over by anaerobic bacteria, which produce obnoxious or toxic compounds such as methane and hydrogen sulfide. The water is then both a public nuisance and unfit for use.

To estimate how much sewage can safely be emptied into a river or lake, it is necessary to know the purifying capacity of its water. This depends on how much oxygen is dissolved in the water. This in turn depends on the surface area, since oxygen dissolves only in the top three-quarters of an inch. Turbulent rivers have a greater surface area than smooth-surfaced rivers and are thus more self-purifying. Slow rivers, such as the Thames, are too smooth to cope with large amounts of sewage. Equally important is knowing the quality of the waste—that is, how much oxygen it requires for decomposition. One type of waste may well require ten times more oxygen than another. The strength of a waste is measured by its *biochemical oxygen demand* (BOD), which is the amount of oxygen it requires for decomposition.

We now describe how sewage is treated prior to discharging it into rivers and lakes, for this, in a sense, is the first stage in water treatment.

Sewage consists of domestic waste together with industrial effluents that are emptied into sewers. In many countries, industry is encouraged to use the sewers for disposal, rather than rivers and lakes. Some towns on the coast still discharge raw sewage into the sea without any treatment, although this is now discouraged. Inland cities, however, have no alternative but to discharge waste along sewers to sewage treatment plants. The first stage in treatment depends on whether sewers also carry storm water—that is, rain that runs off pavements, roads, and roofs. Most cities and suburbs built in recent times have separate sewers and storm drains to relieve the load on their sewage plants. But most cities built their sewers many years ago to transport both sewage and storm water, and it is now uneconomic to convert them into separate systems. Sewage plants therefore usually have *storm water tanks* to store the large bulk of rain-swollen sewage. During dry weather, sewage from these tanks is fed to the plant in amounts that can conveniently be dealt with.

The sewage first passes through *screens* to trap large pieces of wood, rags, wire, and such material. It then passes to *grit tanks*, where grit and sand settle out, thus avoiding blocked pipes and tanks, and preventing unnecessary wear on pumps later on. Leaving the grit tanks, sewage passes to *primary sedimentation tanks*, where about 50 per cent of the suspended solids settle out to form *sludge*. The BOD is also reduced here by about half. Some works mix chemicals, such as alum or ferric sulfate, with the raw sewage to produce a thick mat that drags down solids. This method reduces the suspended solids by about 70 per cent and the BOD by about 85 per cent. Primary sedimentation tanks do not remove dissolved solids. Nor do they remove *colloids*, which are tiny insoluble particles that remain as a cloudy suspension.

What we have just described is called *primary treatment*: It produces sludge, and a liquid called *settled sewage*. Treatment may go no further than this, the settled sewage simply being discharged into a river. This is feasible, of course, only when the river is capable of purifying it. In most plants, however, settled sewage undergoes some *secondary treatment* to reduce the remaining suspended solids and to reduce colloids and dissolved organic matter. There are

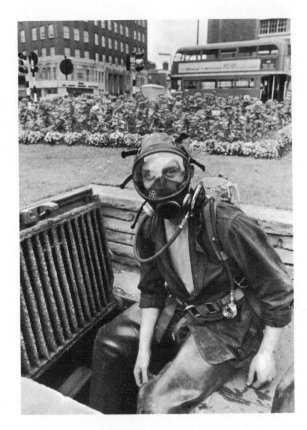

Above: A workman climbs out of a sewer in the heart of London. Breathing apparatus protects him from noxious gases, such as methane and hydrogen sulfide. The London sewer (top right) gives an idea of the size of these channels, many of which were once streams and rivers.

In the trickle filter (below right), revolving arms spray settled sewage onto beds of stones. Here microorganisms oxidize the organic matter until sewage reaches the required degree of purity.

two main methods of secondary treatment—both of which rely on microorganisms to decompose compounds in much the same way as takes place in the soil and in rivers. The process is merely speeded up by having controlled and well-oxygenated conditions. With *trickling filters*, rotating arms spray settled sewage slowly over beds of broken stones. A variety of microorganisms soon find a home on these stones and oxidize the settled sewage to a high purity. The degree of purity may be decided by the authority concerned, one of whose jobs is to calculate

how much sewage a river can take. The treated settled sewage, together with slime deposits that have come off the stones, then passes to a sedimentation tank for clarification. Trickling filters are more suitable for rural areas because they take up a lot of space. They are also ideal where there is a shortage of labor because they need very little supervision.

Sewage treatment plants in cities normally use the *activated sludge* process, which takes up less space. Activated sludge tanks are more sensitive to change and to certain pollutants than trickling filters. They thus need constant, skilled supervision, which is more available in towns. In this process, settled sewage is mixed with sludge that contains microorganisms, and the whole mixture is agitated and oxygenated by compressed air for about 10 hours to encourage rapid decomposition. The mixture then flows to sedimentation tanks, where the sludge settles out. The upper liquid part is discharged into lakes or rivers. A portion of the sludge is then returned to the activated sludge tanks to start a biological decomposition of the new incoming settled sewage.

To produce a reasonably pure settled sewage is no great task. Once produced it can be discharged through pipes (if necessary, by pumping) or made to flow along open channels, called *culverts*. By far the greatest problem in sewage treatment is disposing of the sludge, which can be neither pumped to, nor dumped into, lakes and rivers. *Raw sludge*, which forms in storm tanks and in all sedimentation tanks, is about 96 per cent water, and this is almost impossible to remove economically. Small communities often spread raw sludge on the land, or place it in open lagoons, but decomposition by either method may take several years. Urban areas use a much quicker method by placing raw sludge in *sludge digestion tanks*, where it is digested anaerobically by microorganisms in carefully controlled conditions. In cold tanks, the process takes about four months, but if the tanks are maintained at about 32°c., digestion takes about a month. The methane gas produced during digestion is collected and used to heat the digestion tanks, and to drive pumps, air compressors, and generators. It may even be fed into a gas supply system.

Digested sludge is still about 96 per cent water, but at least it is inoffensive and it can be dried.

The cheapest means of disposal for coastal plants is to dump it by ship into the sea. Sometimes a proportion is used to fill in low-lying land, such as marshes and disused gravel pits. Another method of disposal has recently become common through advances in agriculture, which require that the soil should be conditioned throughout the year. Digested sludge is applied to the land to provide humus and vital chemicals, and both farmer and sewage-plant manager are happy. Most digested sludge, however, has to have some water removed before disposal, so that it ends up with a water content of about 50 per cent and is therefore less bulky. This is usually done by laying sludge on *sludge drying beds*, made of sand and gravel, through which the water seeps and is collected by drains. The dried sludge is then often sold as compost. Raw sludge may also be dewatered by heating, or burned with fuel—methods that are expensive and common mainly in parts of America.

Above: An aerial view of the Crossness sewage plant, London. Below: Its plan. After sewage passes through screens to remove large objects, it goes to storm tanks. From these, it passes to primary sedimentation tanks, where many of the solids settle out to form sludge, leaving a liquid part called settled sewage. The latter passes to activated sludge tanks to reduce organic matter further. The sludge settles out in final sedimentation tanks. Raw sludge from all tanks is treated in digestion tanks, and then dumped into the sea.

Treatment in an activated sludge tank (top left) is the other way of dealing with settled sewage. Aeration and agitation encourage the rapid decomposition of organic matter by microorganisms.

Bottom left: A sludge drying bed covered with digested sludge. Water seeps through sand and is removed by underdrains. A reduction in water content from about 97 to 50 per cent makes residue more compact for disposal.

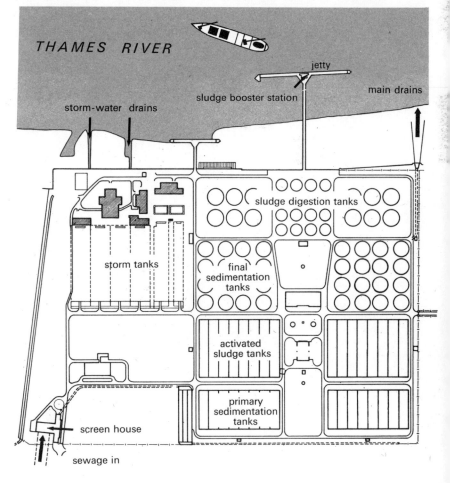

In this chapter we have discussed the treatment of sewage first because the first stage in water treatment is really the prevention of gross pollution. We have to face the fact that most sources of water are polluted and contain water that has been used at least once. As demand grows this use and re-use is bound to increase. We now describe how water is treated to make it suitable for domestic and industrial consumption. It is actually possible to make any water fit for use, no matter how polluted, but not necessarily at an economical price. There are several methods of treating water, the choice depending on the quantity of water required and the type and intensity of the pollution. The easiest water to treat is that from many springs and wells, which require only a precautionary sterilization with chlorine. Many upland lakes and reservoirs in unpopulated areas also provide clean water, so long as it is not polluted on its way to the treatment plants. In lakes and reservoirs, much of the suspended solids settles out. How much and how soon depends on the size and weight of the suspended particles; some very fine particles never settle out. In addition, all kinds of bacteria gradually die, so that 97 per cent have disappeared after about 30 days' storage. Finally, many inorganic and organic compounds are oxidized, and both color and hardness are reduced. These same advantages apply to the storage of even highly polluted river water in storage reservoirs, as in London.

Prolonged storage, however, does encourage the growth of algae, and outbursts are apt to occur just at the time of peak demand in the summer. Algae are rarely harmful to health, but they can produce unpleasant tastes and odors, and clog sand filter beds. Many waterworks try to keep down algal outbursts by adding chemicals such as copper sulfate, potassium permanganate, and chlorine to lakes and reservoirs, but in practice this does not always work.

At the treatment works, water is usually filtered to remove or reduce suspended solids, color, bacteria, algae, and various salts. The oldest method of filtration is by the use of *slow sand filter beds*. These became common in England after 1829, although various types of filter bed had been in use for thousands of years. Slow sand filter beds consist of about two to

Above: A close-up view of part of a rapid gravity filter. The beds are cleaned by driving compressed air up through the sand. The loosened dirt is then flushed to the surface by water. The dirt is washed away by water flowing across the surface of the bed.

three feet of sand resting on about two feet of gravel. As water slowly passes through the sand, a jellylike film forms on the surface (p. 32), which efficiently strains out bacteria and particles in the water. Clean water is drawn off through perforated drains beneath the gravel. Eventually, the film becomes so clogged that the flow of water almost stops. How soon this happens depends on how polluted the water is, and especially on how many algae it contains. Slow sand beds therefore have to be cleaned frequently by taking them out of service and scraping off the dirty layer of sand, usually by hand. This sand is washed for re-use later.

The normal flow through slow sand beds of only 2.4 gallons per square foot per hour requires the beds to have a large surface area and so they take up a considerable amount of space. During algal outbursts, frequent pauses for cleaning reduce the output of water still further. Even so, some cities continue to use slow filter beds. London has 150 acres of them, built many years ago when land and labor were cheap. London has found it convenient to continue their use, but it no longer uses them alone. Now water is

first passed through *rapid sand filter beds* at the rate of about 120–180 gallons per square foot per hour to remove most of the larger solids, which lightens the burden on the slow filter beds. As with slow sand filters, water flows through rapid sand filter beds by gravity, but they take up less room and are easily cleaned by mechanical methods. The film is loosened by passing air and then water upward through the beds; the upper layer is then mechanically scraped. Some treatment plants use *microstrainers* instead of rapid filters. These consist of fine-meshed screens constructed in the form of revolving drums through which water passes. Particles, including algae, are left on the screen and are continuously flushed away. Primary treatment by rapid sand filters or microstrainers is now in common use as an aid to slow sand filters.

Sand filter beds alone are not effective for water that contains fine silt, or various tastes and colors. Colored matter and tastes pass straight through the beds, while the silt quickly blocks them. This happens especially in peaty moorland areas. In parts of the tropics a stream may turn a coffee color in minutes during heavy rain and

Above left: A slow sand filter bed under construction, showing sand, gravel, and porous underdrains that receive the filtered water. Seepage is so slow through slow sand filters that a much larger area is needed than with rapid sand filters (above right).

carry 50 times more silt than ever occurs in England or America. For this reason, America departed in the early 1900's from the traditional European practice, and adopted a method of *chemical treatment*, which has now spread throughout the world. In this process, a coagulant such as aluminum sulfate is mixed with the water entering the tanks. This clumps the solids together, including colloids and bacteria, into groups heavy enough to settle out. One type of chemical treatment tank is about 30 feet deep and shaped like an inverted pyramid. The coagulant forms a stationary sludge blanket about 10 feet thick through which the water passed. Water is pumped upward with a high initial velocity, which decreases near the surface and just prevents the blanket from falling. A highly turbid and colored water passing through such a blanket is clarified and is led away at the surface. The sludge and trapped solids are periodically removed and dried. Various coagulants are available, and are supplemented by other substances, such as sodium alginate (from seaweed) and activated silica, to strengthen the blanket. After treatment with coagulants, the water is always passed through rapid or slow sand filters.

Rapid sand filters are of two types: the open *gravity filter*, in which water seeps down by gravity, and the closed *pressure filter*, where water is *forced* through a bed of sand and gravel. The term *pressure filter* means that water flows through the bed at some pressure. As with gravity types, there is still a loss of pressure, but the process is faster, yielding as much as 720 gallons per square foot per hour. Pressure filters are easier to install than gravity types, but are more liable to fail.

The treatment described above removes most of the bacteria, but some may get through—enough to cause very unpleasant epidemics. The final stage in water treatment is therefore sterilization, usually with chlorine. This was first used to sterilize water in 1897 (in the form of calcium hypochlorite), but it was not until the 1930's that its use became widespread. In developed countries today, all domestic water is sterilized. Although chlorine is a very poisonous gas, small concentrations of dissolved chlorine have no known harmful effect on man, yet it is fatal to microorganisms. Used at a concentration of 0.1 parts of chlorine in a million parts of water (0.1 p.p.m.), it both kills bacteria and removes colors from the water. The actual concentration of chlorine and time of contact with water required depend on the degree of pollution, and should result in no *Escherichia coli* in 100 cc. of water. Although this human, intestinal bacterium is harmless, it is usually present in water. The chances are that if this type is

1

2

eliminated, all the harmful bacteria will be killed, too.

The only disadvantage with chlorine is that it imparts a taste to water if there is too much residual chlorine left. Sometimes it also produces unpleasant tastes by combining with certain types of decayed plant matter, particularly algae. These tastes are almost impossible to remove economically. Tastes are sometimes said to be avoided by using the chloramination process, in which both ammonia and chlorine are added, but this is not altogether successful. One excellent method is *superchlorination*, in which a high concentration of chlorine (about 7 p.p.m.) thoroughly sterilizes the water and removes any residual color and taste. The chlorine is then removed by adding sulfur dioxide to the water.

Chlorine is the best compromise between cheapness and effectiveness. Much better sterilizers exist, such as iodine, bromine, and ultraviolet rays, but they are so costly that they are only used for small quantities of water in special situations. The only real rival to chlorine is ozone (O_2), which is used mainly in France. This is more expensive than chlorine and its power of sterilization is not quite so high, but it does not produce taste problems and it gives water a very pleasant sparkle. Once the reliability of ozone is well established, it will doubtless displace chlorine for those people who consider that a pleasant, sparkling water is worth the small extra cost.

At some stage of treatment, it is often necessary to correct excessive hardness, softness, alkalinity, acidity, and persistent tastes. Temporary hardness is due mainly to the bicarbonates of calcium and magnesium, which the domestic consumer can partially remove by boiling. Permanent hardness is due mainly to the sulfates of calcium and magnesium and is more difficult to remove. The degree of hardness is measured by the ability of water to destroy soap and produce scum. Hard water also produces scale in boilers, kettles, and hot-water pipes, and is not good for cooking vegetables. There are two methods of softening water: precipitation with chemicals, and ion exchange (see Appendix, p. 148). In the first method, lime, in the form of CaO or $Ca(OH)_2$, is added to the water. This causes precipitation of the bicarbonates as insoluble compounds, which are then removed. Sometimes soda ash is also added to precipitate the sulfates. With ion exchange, water is passed through a bed of granules of zeolite, a substance that has the remarkable property of being able to exchange the calcium and magnesium in the water for sodium contained in the zeolite. The water then contains as much mineral matter as before but in the form of sodium bicarbonate and sulfate that are not hardness-forming.

3

4

Four stages in the chemical treatment of a turbid water: (1), Aluminum sulfate is thoroughly mixed with the water, with which it reacts to form large particles, or floc (2), of insoluble aluminum hydroxide. Impurities adhere to the floc, which also aggregates many colloids into particles large enough to settle. After most of the floc and colloids have settled (3), the partially clarified water is passed through sand filters to produce clear, potable water (4).

Zeolites, commonly used for domestic water softeners, are not used by waterworks so much as is the lime-soda softening process.

Natural soft water occurs when rainwater flows over very insoluble rock, and it is pleasant to use in the home. But it is more likely than hard water to dissolve dangerous substances, such as lead and copper from pipes. Soft water is often acid, as in moorland areas where organic acids from decaying plants dissolve in the water. Acidity may also be caused by high concentrations of dissolved carbon dioxide. Acid water is very corrosive and is neutralized with lime.

Certain salts and tastes are not entirely removed by the methods of water treatment that we have described so far. Sometimes costly techniques have to be employed. Common salt (NaCl) cannot be removed economically, and the only remedy is to dilute the water with non-salty water. Iron, manganese, and copper produce metallic tastes, while certain industrial wastes have very tenacious tastes and odors. Ozone deals with some of these troubles. Aeration, by a fountain or by cascading water over small dams, is also used to remove iron, manganese, carbon dioxide, and some tastes. The best taste-remover of all, however, is activated carbon. One cubic inch of this possesses a surface area of over 20,000 square yards, on which substances in the water are held, or adsorbed. Beds of granulated carbon are often used in large ships and have the special advantage of removing phenols, which are extremely offensive. Carbon used in waterworks is usually in powder form. At one time, Los Angeles forced reclaimed sewage into the ground, pumped it up, and then passed it through carbon. The water was said to taste better than from the ordinary supply.

There are many variations in water treatment. New York's water, like that of Manchester, England, is not filtered at all, only sterilized, and occasionally aerated. At the opposite extreme, we have the Amsterdam waterworks, which has the misfortune to have to deal with the Rhine where it ends its journey in Holland. To produce a palatable water from this river, the following steps are performed in sequence: aeration, rapid filtration, aeration, chlorination (at 6 parts per million), aeration, artificial recharge underground through sand dunes for two to three months, aeration, activated carbon, rapid filtration, slow sand filtration, aeration, chlorination. Even after this all-out attack, bad tastes sometimes get through!

Finally, we deal with the treatment of industrial water—sometimes a more difficult proposition than preparing water for domestic consumption. Some industries take water directly from rivers and lakes, in which case the initial treatment follows the same lines as for domestic water. Water that is taken from the public mains sometimes has to undergo additional treatment. The domestic consumer does not object to moderately hard water, whereas industry often requires water of almost zero hardness. The salts that make water hard form encrustations in boilers, pipes, and heat exchangers, which decreases the conductivity of the heat-transferring surfaces, resulting in overheating and occasional damage. Hardness is also harmful in the laundering and textile trades, because scum damages and discolors fabrics.

The lime-soda method of softening, already mentioned, is often used by industry. The ordinary ion-exchange process using zeolites is even more efficient, producing water of almost zero hardness. But with both these methods, salts remain in the water. Some industries, ranging from power plants to the makers of transistors, need to remove all the salts from water, by a process called *demineralization*. This is an elaboration of the ion-exchange process (Appendix, p. 149) in which one zeolite removes the cations—mainly calcium, magnesium, iron, sodium, etc. Another zeolite removes the anions —sulfate, bicarbonate, nitrate, and so on.

As well as forming encrustations, water can also be very corrosive at high temperatures. The main cause of this corrosion is dissolved oxygen and carbon dioxide, so these gases have to be removed. Finally, some industries are also concerned with the organic matter and microorganisms in water, but not usually for health reasons. Surface water generally contains small amounts of organic matter, even after treatment, and these damage the zeolites used in ion exchange. Organic matter may be removed by hydrogen peroxide and activated carbon. Then we have the slimes and encrustations that tend to form in pipes due to the presence of organic matter, and iron and sulfur bacteria. One way of eliminating these is by thorough chlorination.

Fifty-four million gallons a day cascade from the
water tower (above) in Grafham Water, England.
The tower was built in order to investigate its
effect on circulating and aerating the lake.

11 The Future

We can now discuss the future of our water supplies, and consider some recent warnings that before the next century there will be a widespread shortage. Taking the inhabited world as a whole, there is sufficient fresh water to support a far larger world population than exists at present. The problem is rather one of storage and transport. As we have seen, many countries have adequate water resources only in one region or at one time of the year. It is for these reasons that only a very small fraction of the world's fresh water is economically available. As future demands increase, however, it will become more and more necessary to overcome the unequal distribution and timing of rainfall. More reservoirs will have to be built to store the wet season's surplus, although in some regions it may well be cheaper to store surplus water in aquifers by some method of artificial recharge. Most of the sources and reservoir sites that are close to big cities are already exploited, so we shall have to seek out more distant catchment areas in which to build reservoirs. This implies even longer aqueducts than have been built so far.

Projects that involve distant reservoirs and long aqueducts take many years to design and build, and it is no good starting them only when the supplies run short. The safe way is to anticipate demand by as much as 30 years ahead, otherwise very serious shortages are bound to occur. One particularly ambitious and romantic plan that attempts to provide for the needs of the twenty-first century is called NAWAPA (short for North American Water and Power Alliance), and was conceived by the Ralph M. Parsons Company, of Los Angeles. The huge water surplus of northwest Canada and the United States (including Alaska), which at present pours into the sea, would be stored in reservoirs at high elevation. From these, 64 trillion gallons would flow annually to 7 provinces of Canada, 33 states of the Union, and 3 states of Mexico, through a system of tunnels, pipes, canals, and rivers. As well as helping industry and the domestic consumer, this project would irrigate 40 million acres of the arid northwestern states of the United States, triple the agricultural land of Mexico, feed a huge waterway from the Great Lakes of America across Canada and thus benefit transport, and at the same time maintain the levels of the Great Lakes. In addition to all this, the project would generate enormous quantities of electrical power.

The project is estimated to cost at least $925 billion. A preliminary period of 10 years is provided for discussion leading to interstate agreements, and construction is estimated to take at least 30 years. The go-ahead has not yet been given. One of the many reasons is that Canada may not agree to share its water, although no more than 20 per cent of the Canadian surplus would be exploited. But some large project will have to be decided on fairly soon if the western United States is to continue its rapid expansion and high standard of living into the next century. The same considerations apply to other countries.

The transport of water from distant lakes and reservoirs should be considered only after every effort has been made to use existing supplies several times over. Already it is impossible to meet demands in many countries without using some water more than once. This practice will have to be encouraged if water is not to become scarce. Not all water, of course, is re-usable. Much used for irrigation and by some industries is lost by absorption, evaporation, or both. But most water used by industry and the domestic consumer can be treated and then returned to rivers and lakes for further use.

The North American Water and Power Alliance is a project (above) suggested for increasing water supplies to the drier parts of the United States, Canada, and Mexico. The plan proposes to divert 64 trillion gallons annually from northwestern Canada and United States, via rivers, canals, and aqueducts. Some such ambitious project will be needed to meet the predicted demands of the 21st century. Since it would take up to 50 years to negotiate and construct, planning should not be delayed.

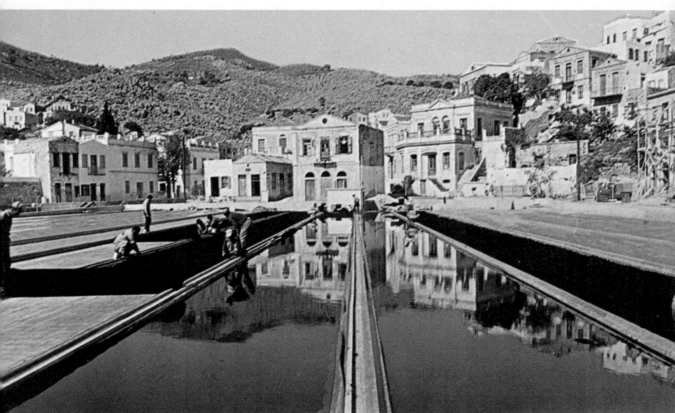

Water will run seriously short in the future unless as much as possible is re-used. The Lincoln Center fountain in New York City (top) recirculates water over and over again. Above: Solar distillation plant under construction on the Greek island of Syme. Small reservoirs of sea water are covered with plastic sheets, which will trap 4800 gallons per day. This method is suitable only for small populations.

Most industrial effluents contain pollutants, and the natural process of purifying rivers and lakes rarely restores the water to its original quality. Even the most careful treatment of sewage, for example, does not remove sodium chloride. If several sewage plants discharge into one river, the salt content progressively increases downstream. This may not matter with large rivers, where pollutants are diluted, but they may reach dangerous concentrations when the river level falls. Waterworks naturally try to obtain water upstream from the sewage plants, but this is not possible for long rivers such as the Rhine, Thames, and Danube, with towns along much of their length. Thus the maximum re-use of water is economic only when industrial effluents and sewage are properly treated before discharge and when they are adequately diluted by the natural river flow.

One way of re-using water is to treat sewage and then pass the effluent to a storage reservoir at the water treatment plant, where it is made suitable for consumption. One American town has already been forced to do this, going through the cycle of water-sewage-water as many as 18 times before finally returning it to the river. The main problem here is the elimination of tastes, but new techniques may overcome this.

The re-use of water by industry is particularly important because of the enormous quantities involved. Water may be used once by a factory, or it may be recycled as many as 30 times, at each stage undergoing treatment to remove impurities. Without this re-use within the factory, water-

works would have to find new sources of water and build larger treatment plants much sooner than they otherwise would do. Furthermore, industrial effluents are often discharged into sewers, and so more sewage plants would have to be built as well. By placing greater demands on both treatment and sewage plants, the price of water to industry would increase, so it is in their interest to re-use water.

One recent and exciting means of increasing our fresh-water resources is by *desalination*, which bypasses the normal hydrological cycle. The natural conversion of salt water to fresh has been known for over two thousand years. The Greeks knew that the sun evaporated fresh water from the sea, and that this later fell to earth as rain. But only recently has man been able to desalinate sea water in large quantities at an acceptable cost. The simplest method of desalination is *solar distillation*, where solar energy is harnessed to evaporate sea water. The sea water is pumped into a reservoir that has a black lining to absorb the sun's rays, and that is covered with a transparent plastic sheet. Fresh-water vapor condenses on the underside and runs down into a trough. Even though solar energy is free, the cost of a thousand gallons to one Greek island is supposed to be about $2.10. This is still very cheap compared with the previous cost of about $6.70. for water shipped from the mainland. Perhaps this is an appropriate moment to mention the cost of water before we discuss desalination further. The acceptable cost depends on the alternative sources of

Dracones (interior and exterior views) are used to haul about 20 million gallons of fresh water annually to the Greek islands. Unlike the solar still they can be used to provide more water if necessary.

supply. If there is no alternative, the price does not enter the argument, for the simple reason that water is essential to life.

Solar distillation is an unusual method of desalination and is economic only in regions with very long periods of sunshine and no other source of water. Other methods require an artificial source of energy, because when salts dissolve in water, heat energy is given off. In order to separate water and salts, a certain definite amount of energy must therefore be put back. This quota of energy fixes the theoretical minimum cost of desalination at about four cents per thousand gallons. In practice, the cost is much higher because heat escapes at all stages and no machine works at 100 per cent efficiency. A more realistic price, allowing for the capital outlay, running costs, and expected life of the plant, is about $1.00 per thousand gallons, compared with about 18 cents for conventional methods of supply.

The most common method of desalination is by a process called *multistage flash distillation.* Sea water is heated to between 90° and 120°C. and then sprayed into a vessel maintained at reduced pressure. Now, the lower the atmospheric pressure, the lower the temperature at which water boils. Therefore, in this first vessel water boils, or *flashes*, instantaneously. The

remaining brine, which is now cooler because of heat loss, then passes to another vessel. There the water again boils immediately because this vessel is at an even lower pressure than the first. Sea water may pass on through as many as 40 vessels at progressively lower pressure until the residual brine reaches such a low temperature that it will no longer boil quickly enough. The fresh-water vapor is condensed by water-cooled pipes. As it condenses, it gives out latent heat, returning some of the original heat to the fresh, incoming brine.

The most costly part of flash distillation is heating the water. It is not really economical for a desalination plant to heat its own water, except in ships, where the very high cost of $1.90 per thousand gallons is still less than the loss of revenue that would occur if cargo space were given over to fresh-water storage. On land the usual practice is to use the residual heat in steam that has passed through the turbines of a power station. This "waste heat," which is about 120°C., is of no use to the power station but is suitable for heating sea water. In any case, it would be impracticable to use steam above 120°C. without causing excessive encrustations in the heat exchange pipes. The most efficient desalination thus combines the production of electricity and fresh water. Recently, nuclear

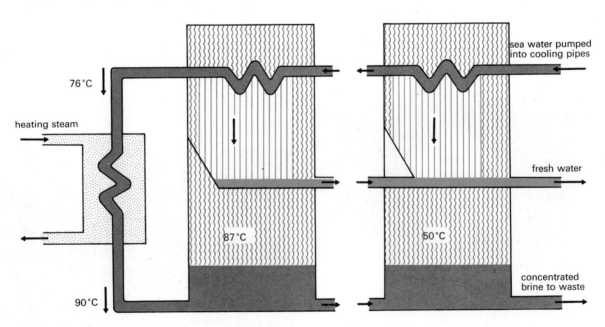

Above: Diagram shows first and last stages of a multi-stage flash distillation plant with 12 chambers. Sea water (gray) is heated to 90°C. by "waste" steam from a power station. It then passes to first chamber, where low pressure makes it boil immediately. Fresh-water vapor (blue dots) is condensed by cooling pipes, and it collects in a trough. Sea water gradually cools as it passes through the 12 chambers, but still boils because there is a pressure drop between each chamber. For economical use of heat, sea water is first used in cooling pipes. The cooling water flows in opposite direction to boiling brine so that latent heat released by condensing vapor preheats cooling water before it is heated to 90°C.

energy has entered the scene. Israel and California, for example, are planning to build atomic reactors to produce electricity, using waste heat for converting salt water to fresh.

Several other methods of desalination exist, but none competes with flash distillation for the production of large quantities of water at reasonable cost. Freeze-separation, for example, makes use of the fact that ice crystals from frozen sea water consist of fresh water. Another method, called *electrodialysis*, is the opposite of distillation: It removes the salt from sea water, leaving fresh water behind. Such methods are only suitable for water of low salt content and may prove very useful in arid lands where there is a supply of salty water.

It is impossible to predict exactly what part desalination will play in the future. It will never completely replace existing sources, and it is certainly too expensive for irrigation and for inland communities. Desalination is appropriate for those situations in which a special combination of circumstances make it the cheapest—and often the only—method. Kuwait in the Persian Gulf, for instance, has no natural fresh water, an abundance of cheap oil, and the highest average income per person in the world. Their plant (producing 15.6 million gallons daily) is the obvious answer. The island of Guernsey, whose main income comes from horticulture, has little underground water and not enough space to store surface water. In this situation it was worthwhile converting sea water to supplement the upland supply during the brief period of dry summer weather. Undoubtedly, more and more places with special problems will install desalination plants as the demands of industry and the domestic consumer increase.

If we have not mentioned in this chapter any prospect of discovering *new* ways of increasing our future water supplies, it is because these probably do not exist. There is no means of manufacturing water in large quantities without destroying some other equally valuable commodity. We have to rely on trapping natural precipitation or, if we are prepared to pay for it, on desalination. In other words, we can do no more than develop and perfect our present methods of obtaining fresh water.

We have seen that by re-using water as much as possible, and by reducing waste and leakage, water can be made to go a surprisingly long way. We have also seen that there is abundant fresh water available to store and transport. As living standards improve and as populations increase, we shall sooner or later be faced with paying, directly or indirectly, for new and costly projects. And we are in no position to resent the prospect. For most of us a constant supply of clean water when and where we want it, costing only a few cents per ton, is a real bargain, and we can count our blessings. It is in the underdeveloped countries that the problems are more serious. Waterworks require massive expenditure, and money is just what these countries do not have. The necessary finance can come to them only through foreign aid. It seems only fair that the developed countries help to provide the means whereby every man, woman, and child on earth has an adequate water supply.

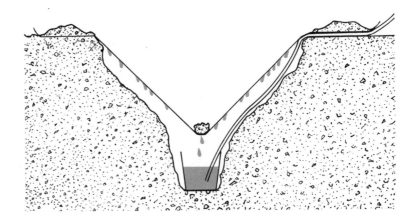

The recent invention—by scientists of the U.S. Water Conservation Laboratory, Arizona—of the "survival still" ensures that a man can now have enough to drink even in the driest desert. He simply places a bucket at the bottom of a three-foot-diameter hole and arranges a plastic sheet, as in diagram (right). The sun raises temperature of air and soil beneath sheet, hastening evaporation of soil water. When air is saturated, vapor condenses on underside of sheet and runs into bucket. At least one pint a day is obtained.

LIME TREATMENT

Removal of temporary hardness due to calcium and magnesium bicarbonates:

Impurity		*Reagent*		*Precipitate*		
$Ca(HCO_3)_2$	$+$	$Ca(OH)_2$ $\longrightarrow$		$2CaCO_3$	$+$	$2H_2O$
calcium bicarbonate		hydrated lime		calcium carbonate		

Impurity		*Reagent*		*Precipitate*		*Precipitate*
$Mg(HCO_3)_2$		$2Ca(OH)_2$ $\longrightarrow$		$Mg(OH)_2$	$+$	$2CaCO_3 + 2H_2O$
magnesium bicarbonate		hydrated lime		magnesium hydroxide		calcium carbonate

Lime also removes carbon dioxide from raw water:

Impurity		*Reagent*		*Precipitate*		
CO_2	$+$	$Ca(OH)_2$ $\longrightarrow$		$CaCO_3$	$+$	H_2O
carbon dioxide		hydrated lime		calcium carbonate		

Removal of permanent hardness due to magnesium salts, e.g. $MgSO_4$:

Impurity		*Reagent*				*Precipitate*
$MgSO_4$	$+$	$Ca(OH)_2$ $\longrightarrow$		$CaSO_4$	$+$	$Mg(OH)_2$
magnesium sulfate		hydrated lime		calcium sulfate		magnesium hydroxide

The soluble calcium sulfate formed by this process, as well as the calcium sulfate in original raw water, is removed by reaction with soda ash:

SODA ASH TREATMENT

Impurity		*Reagent*				*Precipitate*
$CaSO_4$	$+$	Na_2CO_3 $\longrightarrow$		Na_2SO_4	$+$	$CaCO_3$
calcium sulfate		soda ash		sodium sulfate		calcium carbonate

The soluble sodium sulfate produced is not hardness forming.

The chemical formulas (above) show how water is softened by the lime-soda method. This converts the soluble salts that cause temporary hardness (mainly calcium and magnesium bicarbonates) and permanent hardness (mainly calcium and magnesium sulfates) into soluble salts. The resulting precipitate is then removed. The salts that remain in the water after treatment do not produce hard water.

CATION EXCHANGER

ANION EXCHANGER

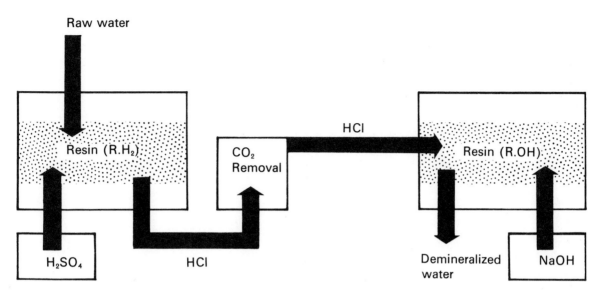

Raw water

Resin (R.H$_2$)

CO$_2$ Removal

HCl

Resin (R.OH)

H$_2$SO$_4$

HCl

Demineralized water

NaOH

Acid for Regeneration

Alkali for Regeneration

Reaction inside resin (R.H$_2$), e.g. for MgCl$_2$
MgCl$_{2+}$ + R.H$_2$ → R.Mg + 2HCl
thus Mg^{++} from MgCl$_2$ is removed

Reaction inside resin (R.OH)
HCl + R.OH → RHCl + H$_2$O
thus Cl$^-$ from Mg$_|$Cl$_2$ is removed

Regeneration of resin
R.Mg + H$_2$SO$_4$ ⟶ MgSO$_4$ + R.H$_2$
　　　　　regenerating　　flushed
　　　　　acid　　　　　　away

Regeneration of resin
R.Cl + NaOH → R.OH + NaCl
　　　regenerating　　flushed
　　　alkali　　　　　away

Industry removes almost all salts from water by using ion-exchange process (above). First, cations (positively charged ions) in raw water are exchanged for hydrogen ions from cation-exchange resin; thus all salts in raw water are converted to acids. Water and acids then pass through anion-exchange resin, where anions (negatively charged ions) are exchanged for hydroxylions. Resins are periodically regenerated with acid or alkali.

Index

Credits

Key to illustration position
    (T) top, (C) center, (B) bottom,
    (L) left, (R) right

Endpapers: Photos Geoffrey Drury
Frontispiece: Photo Marc Riboud/
Magnum

Page
13 Paul Popper Ltd.
16 (BR) British Museum
18 Photos U.S. Department of
    Agriculture, Soil Conserva-
    tion Service
19 (R) Photo Ken Coton,
    © Aldus Books
22 Photo Paul Almasy
28 Mansell Collection
31 (B) Photo John Hillaby
33 (BL) Reproduced from
    "Worms in Man" by
    permission of The Wellcome
    Foundation Ltd.
    (BR) Photo Paul Almasy
35 (T) Hilprecht-Collection of
    the Friedrich-Schiller-
    University, Jena, DDR-
    Germany
    (B) Archaeological Survey of
    India
37 P.A.-Reuter photo
39 (BL) Forest Gate Model
    Laundry Ltd./ photo Mike
    Busselle, © Aldus Books
    (BR) The Permutit Co. Ltd.,
    London
40 *Time* © 1966. Time Inc.
41 Photo Brian Brake/Magnum
43 (B) *Universal Magazine*, 1749
44 (T) Mansell Collection
    (B) By Courtesy of City of
    Birmingham Water
    Department
45 (TL) *Time* © 1965. Time Inc.
    Photo Ben Martin
    (TR) Photo Metropolitan
    Water Board
47 (TL) South Durham Steel &
    Iron Co. Ltd.
53 *Time* © 1965. Time Inc.
    Photo Ben Martin
57-9 (T) Mansell Collection
62 (T) Photo Delwyn Davies
63 (R) WHO photo
65 Photo W. J. Allen
69 (T) Photo David Moore/
    Black Star Inc.
    (BR) Photo Frank Apthorp
70 (TL) Photo J. E. Dayton,
    London
    (TR) and (BL) Photos Paul
    Almasy

155

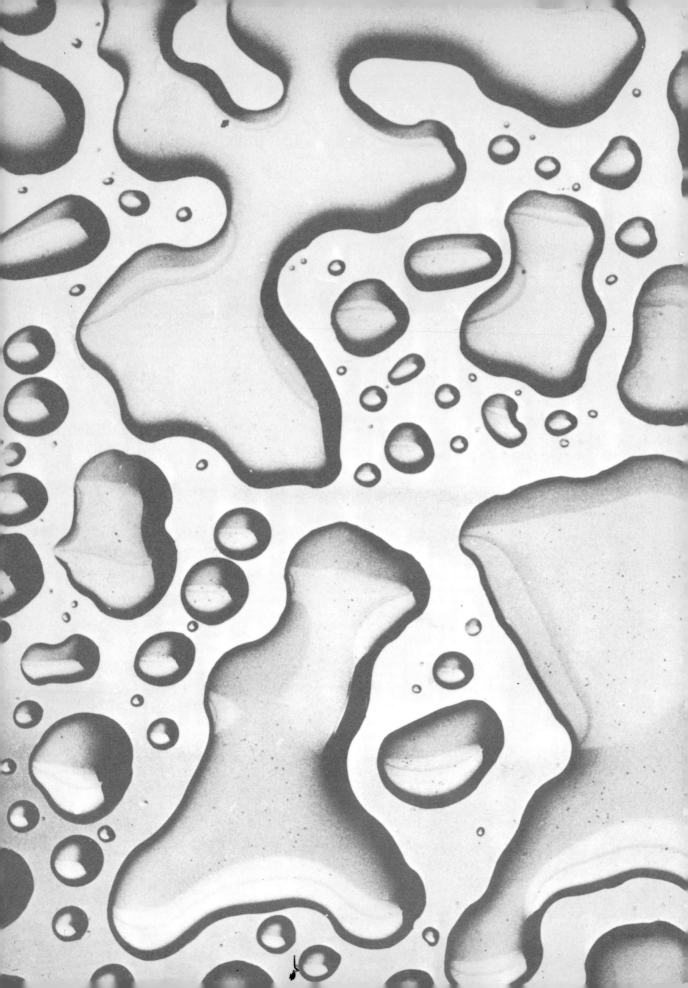